KU-427-501

WORKED EXAMPLES IN ADVANCED ELECTRICAL ENGINEERING

by

K. S. CHAPMAN

B.Sc.(ENG.), A.M.I.E.E., A.M.I.E.R.E.

Senior Lecturer in Electrical Engineering and Electrical Measurements
at The Mid-Essex Technical College, Chelmsford

LONDON

EDWARD ARNOLD (PUBLISHERS) LTD

First published 1964

Made and printed in Great Britain by
William Clowes and Sons, Limited, London and Beccles

PREFACE

This book was written to meet the needs of students preparing for Part III of the Examination of the Institution of Electrical Engineers in the subject of Advanced Electrical Engineering. It should also prove useful to those students studying for Engineering Degrees, Diploma in Technology, post Higher National Diploma courses leading to a particular College award, and similar advanced courses in Advanced Electrical Engineering.

Some of the students in the course in preparation for the Part III of the Institution of Electrical Engineers examination, emanate from the Higher National Certificate courses with their various endorsements. It is mainly for this type of student that this book was written. The correct approach to these questions can only be acquired by individual practice by the student in answering past examination paper questions.

The book does not contain all the questions set in the various papers. It is felt that the greatest need of the student is practice in examples in electrical circuit theory, and so standard bookwork on electric field theory has been omitted.

Examination questions, which may readily be solved by means of Laplace transforms, and matrix algebra seem to present difficulty to many students. It must be pointed out that whilst these two topics are very useful mathematical tools, they can, in some cases, lead to more complicated solutions of problems than those employing well known classical methods. The student is therefore recommended to learn the modern techniques, but not at the expense of forgetting, or ignoring, the well tried methods.

It is too much to hope that no errors exist in this book. Due to the controversial nature of some of the questions alternative solutions may be possible. The intimation of any errors, or alternative solutions, will be gratefully received by the author.

My thanks are due to the Council of the Institution of Electrical Engineers for permission to publish the examination papers, the solutions of which are my responsibility. I am also indebted to the publishers, Edward Arnold Ltd., for the consideration and courtesy extended to me in the preparation of this book.

I am appreciative of the useful suggestions and criticisms made by my colleagues, and last but not least, of the numerous students who unwittingly helped to check the solutions in this book.

K. S. C.

Mid-Essex Technical College.
1963

CONTENTS

SYMBOLS AND ABBREVIATIONS

Symbol	*Term*	*Unit*	*Abbreviation*
Y	Admittance, complex quantity		
Y	Admittance, scalar quantity	mho	
ω	Angular frequency	radian per second	rad/s
n, N	Angular velocity	revolution per second	rev/s
		revolution per minute	rev/min
μ	Amplification factor of a valve		
α	Attenuation coefficient	neper	N
ε	Base of natural logarithms		
C	Capacitance	farad	F
		microfarad	μF
Z_0	Characteristic impedance of a transmission line, or a symmetrical quadripole network	ohm	Ω
Q	Charge or quantity of electricity	coulomb	*C*
		ampere-hour	Ah
q	Instantaneous value of charge		
G	Conductance	mho	
	Current:		
I	Vector quantity		
I	Steady or r.m.s. value	ampere	A
i	Instantaneous value		
I_m	Maximum value		
	Difference of potential:		
V	Vector quantity		
V	Steady or r.m.s. value	volt	V
v	Instantaneous value		
V_m	Maximum value		
	Electromotive force:		
E	Vector quantity		
E	Steady or r.m.s. value	volt	V
e	Instantaneous value		
E_m	Maximum value		

Symbol	*Term*	*Unit*	*Abbreviation*
W	Energy	joule	J
		watt-hour	Wh
		kilowatt-hour	kWh
F	Force	newton	N
f	Frequency	cycle per second	c/s
$\mathbf{Z}$	Impedance, complex quantity		
Z	Impedance, scalar quantity	ohm	Ω
L	Inductance, self	henry	H
M	Inductance, mutual	henry	H
	Logarithm of x to base 10		$\log x$
	Logarithm of x to base ε		$\ln x$
g_m	Mutual conductance of a value	milliampere per volt	mA/V
J	Moment of inertia, polar	kilogramme (metre)^2	kg-m^2
j	Operator 90°		
h or a	Operator 120°		
μ_r	Permeability (relative)		
μ_0	Permeability of free space	henry per metre	H/m
ϵ_r	Permittivity (relative)		
ϵ_0	Permittivity of free space	farad per metre	F/m
β	Phase change coefficient	radian	rad
P	Power	watt	W
		kilowatt	kW
		megawatt	MW
S	Apparent power	volt-ampere	VA
		kilovolt-ampere	kVA
		megavolt-ampere	MVA
Q	Reactive power	var	VAr
$\cos \phi$	Power factor		p.f.
γ	Propagation coefficient		
$\mathbf{X}$	Reactance, complex quantity		
X	Reactance, scalar quantity	ohm	Ω
R	Resistance	ohm	Ω
r_a	Slope resistance of a valve	ohm	Ω
m	Stage gain of an amplifier		
$\mathbf{B}$	Susceptance, complex quantity		
B	Susceptance, scalar quantity	mho	
	Voltage—See Difference of potential or Electromotive force		
λ	Wavelength	metre	m

The following abbreviations have been used to denote the sources from which the problems have been taken:

A.E.E. The Institution of Electrical Engineers Examination Part III in Advanced Electrical Engineering.
A.M-E.C. The Associateship of the Mid-Essex College Examination in Advanced Electrical Engineering.
H.N.D. The Higher National Diploma Examination in Advanced Electrical Engineering (Circuits).

Symbol notation

The symbols used above conform to those recommended by the Institution of Electrical Engineers for use in Electrical Engineering Courses. There is, in addition, the usual use of the heavy Clarendon type to represent vector or complex quantities. Thus $\mathbf{Z} = (R+jX)$. whilst $Z = \sqrt{R^2+X^2}$. It is appreciated that the average student would find this convention difficult to execute in an examination, and it is used in this book for the sake of clarity. In many cases the vector or complex quantities would be easily distinguished from scalar quantities by the context of the solution.

Conventional directions of voltage and current

Many papers and articles have been written about this subject, and it is a well-aired topic in the staff rooms of the electrical lecturers at Technical Colleges and Universities. The topic is too big to be included in a work of this nature. After experience with teaching different circuit conventions over a number of years, the conventions used in the solutions in this book have been selected as they seem to be the most easily understood by the average student. The 'tails' to the arrows are the author's idiosyncracy; they indicate that this end of the arrow is relatively negative with respect to the arrow head, e.g.

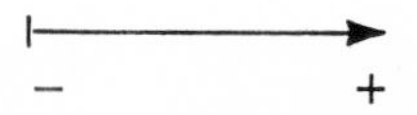

PAPER NO. 1—NOVEMBER 1959

1. Determine the characteristic impedance of the network of reactances shown in the figure below. Show that when the network is terminated by its characteristic impedance, the propagation coefficient γ of the network may be given by the relation:

$$\tanh(\gamma/2) = \sqrt{X_1/X_2}$$

Hence, deduce that if X_1 and X_2 are of opposite sign the network has zero attenuation at all frequencies.

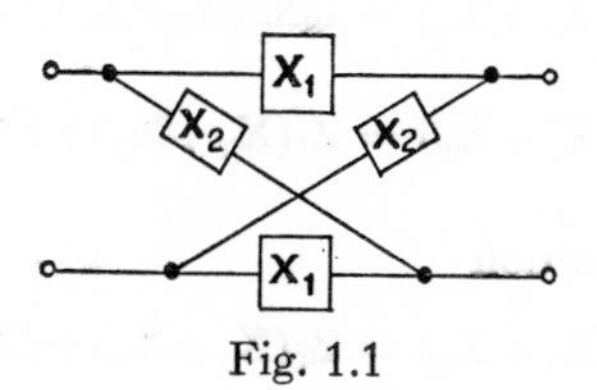

Fig. 1.1

Solution By definition, the characteristic impedance Z_0 is the input impedance of the network when it is terminated in Z_0. The circuit may be analysed more clearly by redrawing as in the figure shown below. Use the conventional directions of voltage and current as indicated.

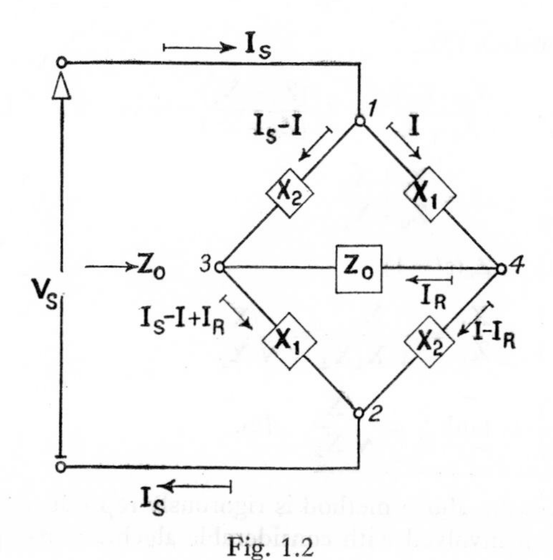

Fig. 1.2

Applying Kirchhoff's second law to the closed meshes 1342 and 1432 in turn:

$$(\mathbf{I_S}-\mathbf{I})\mathbf{X}_2-\mathbf{I_R}\mathbf{Z}_0+(\mathbf{I}-\mathbf{I_R})\mathbf{X}_2 = \mathbf{V_S}$$

and
$$\mathbf{I}\mathbf{X}_1+\mathbf{I_R}\mathbf{Z}_0+(\mathbf{I_S}-\mathbf{I}+\mathbf{I_R})\mathbf{X}_1 = \mathbf{V_S}$$

$$\therefore \mathbf{V_S} = \mathbf{I_S}\mathbf{X}_2-\mathbf{I_R}(\mathbf{Z}_0+\mathbf{X}_2) \tag{1}$$

and
$$\mathbf{V_S} = \mathbf{I_S}\mathbf{X}_1+\mathbf{I_R}(\mathbf{Z}_0+\mathbf{X}_1) \tag{2}$$

From equations (1) and (2),

$$\mathbf{I_R} = \frac{\mathbf{I_S}\mathbf{X}_2-\mathbf{V_S}}{\mathbf{Z}_0+\mathbf{X}_2} = \frac{\mathbf{V_S}-\mathbf{I_S}\mathbf{X}_1}{\mathbf{Z}_0+\mathbf{X}_1} \tag{3}$$

$$\therefore (\mathbf{I_S}\mathbf{X}_2-\mathbf{V_S})(\mathbf{Z}_0+\mathbf{X}_1) = (\mathbf{V_S}-\mathbf{I_S}\mathbf{X}_1)(\mathbf{Z}_0+\mathbf{X}_2)$$

$$\therefore \mathbf{V_S}(\mathbf{Z}_0+\mathbf{X}_1+\mathbf{Z}_0+\mathbf{X}_2) = \mathbf{I_S}\mathbf{X}_2(\mathbf{Z}_0+\mathbf{X}_1)+\mathbf{I_S}\mathbf{X}_1(\mathbf{Z}_0+\mathbf{X}_2)$$

$$\therefore \frac{\mathbf{V_S}}{\mathbf{I_S}}(2\mathbf{Z}_0+\mathbf{X}_1+\mathbf{X}_2) = \mathbf{Z}_0(\mathbf{X}_1+\mathbf{X}_2)+2\mathbf{X}_1\mathbf{X}_2$$

but $\mathbf{V_S}/\mathbf{I_S} = \mathbf{Z}_0$ by definition

$$\therefore \mathbf{Z}_0(2\mathbf{Z}_0+\mathbf{X}_1+\mathbf{X}_2) = \mathbf{Z}_0(\mathbf{X}_1+\mathbf{X}_2)+2\mathbf{X}_1\mathbf{X}_2$$

$$\therefore 2\mathbf{Z}_0^2 = 2\mathbf{X}_1\mathbf{X}_2$$

$$\therefore \mathbf{Z}_0 = \sqrt{\mathbf{X}_1\mathbf{X}_2} \quad \textit{Ans.}$$

By definition,
$$\frac{\mathbf{I_S}}{\mathbf{I_R}} = \varepsilon^{\gamma}$$

Now from equation (3),

$$\mathbf{I_R} = \frac{\mathbf{V_S}-\mathbf{I_S}\mathbf{X}_1}{\mathbf{Z}_0+\mathbf{X}_1} = \mathbf{I_S}\frac{(\mathbf{Z}_0-\mathbf{X}_1)}{(\mathbf{Z}_0+\mathbf{X}_1)} \quad \text{since} \quad \mathbf{V_S} = \mathbf{I_S}\mathbf{Z}_0$$

$$\therefore \frac{\mathbf{I_S}}{\mathbf{I_R}} = \varepsilon^{\gamma} = \frac{\mathbf{Z}_0+\mathbf{X}_1}{\mathbf{Z}_0-\mathbf{X}_1}$$

$$\therefore \mathbf{X}_1(\varepsilon^{\gamma}+1) = \mathbf{Z}_0(\varepsilon^{\gamma}-1)$$

$$\therefore \frac{\varepsilon^{\gamma}-1}{\varepsilon^{\gamma}+1} = \frac{\mathbf{X}_1}{\mathbf{Z}_0} = \frac{\mathbf{X}_1}{\sqrt{\mathbf{X}_1\mathbf{X}_2}} = \sqrt{\frac{\mathbf{X}_1}{\mathbf{X}_2}}$$

$$\therefore \frac{\varepsilon^{\gamma}-1}{\varepsilon^{\gamma}+1} = \tanh\frac{\gamma}{2} = \sqrt{\frac{\mathbf{X}_1}{\mathbf{X}_2}} \quad \textit{Ans.}$$

Note: Unless the above method is rigorously reproduced, the student can find himself involved with considerable algebraic manipulation.

The following method is suggested as a suitable alternative, and not a shorter solution.

Aliter For any 4-terminal network

$$\mathbf{V_S} = \mathbf{AV_R} + \mathbf{BI_R}$$

and

$$\mathbf{I_S} = \mathbf{CV_R} + \mathbf{DI_R}$$

where **A**, **B**, **C**, and **D** are constants for a given network defined as follows:

$$\mathbf{A} = \frac{\mathbf{V_S}}{\mathbf{V_R}} \quad \text{with the termination on open-circuit}$$

$$\mathbf{B} = \frac{\mathbf{V_S}}{\mathbf{I_R}} \quad \text{with the termination on short-circuit}$$

$$\mathbf{C} = \frac{\mathbf{I_S}}{\mathbf{V_R}} \quad \text{with the termination on open-circuit}$$

$$\mathbf{D} = \frac{\mathbf{I_S}}{\mathbf{I_R}} \quad \text{with the termination on short-circuit}$$

For this problem with terminals 3 and 4 on open-circuit,

$$\mathbf{V_R} = \frac{\mathbf{I_S}}{2}(\mathbf{X_2} - \mathbf{X_1}) = \frac{\mathbf{V_S}}{\mathbf{X_2} + \mathbf{X_1}} \cdot (\mathbf{X_2} - \mathbf{X_1})$$

$$\therefore \mathbf{A} = \frac{\mathbf{V_S}}{\mathbf{V_R}} = \frac{\mathbf{X_2} + \mathbf{X_1}}{\mathbf{X_2} - \mathbf{X_1}}$$

Also since

$$\mathbf{V_S} = \frac{\mathbf{I_S}}{2}(\mathbf{X_2} + \mathbf{X_1})$$

$$\therefore \mathbf{C} = \frac{\mathbf{I_S}}{\mathbf{V_R}} = \frac{2}{\mathbf{X_2} - \mathbf{X_1}}$$

With the terminals 3 and 4 on short-circuit,

$$\mathbf{I_R} = \frac{\dfrac{\mathbf{V_S}(\mathbf{X_2} - \mathbf{X_1})}{\mathbf{X_2} + \mathbf{X_1}}}{\dfrac{2\mathbf{X_1}\mathbf{X_2}}{\mathbf{X_2} + \mathbf{X_1}}} = \frac{\mathbf{V_S}(\mathbf{X_2} - \mathbf{X_1})}{2\mathbf{X_1}\mathbf{X_2}}$$

$$\therefore \mathbf{B} = \frac{\mathbf{V_S}}{\mathbf{I_R}} = \frac{2\mathbf{X_1}\mathbf{X_2}}{\mathbf{X_2} - \mathbf{X_1}}$$

Also

$$\mathbf{V_S} = \mathbf{I_S}\frac{2\mathbf{X_1}\mathbf{X_2}}{\mathbf{X_1} + \mathbf{X_2}}$$

$$\therefore \mathbf{D} = \frac{\mathbf{I_S}}{\mathbf{I_R}} = \frac{\mathbf{X}_2+\mathbf{X}_1}{\mathbf{X}_2-\mathbf{X}_1} = \mathbf{A}$$

Now $\quad \dfrac{\mathbf{V_S}}{\mathbf{I_S}} = \dfrac{\mathbf{AV_R}+\mathbf{BI_R}}{\mathbf{CV_R}+\mathbf{DI_R}}$ but since $\mathbf{V_R} = \mathbf{I_R Z_0}$

$$= \frac{\mathbf{AI_R Z_0}+\mathbf{BI_R}}{\mathbf{CI_R Z_0}+\mathbf{DI_R}}$$

$$= \frac{\mathbf{AZ_0}+\mathbf{B}}{\mathbf{CZ_0}+\mathbf{D}} = \mathbf{Z_0} \text{ by definition}$$

$$\therefore \mathbf{Z_0}(\mathbf{CZ_0}+\mathbf{D}-\mathbf{A}) = \mathbf{B}$$

$$\therefore \mathbf{Z_0}^2 = \frac{\mathbf{B}}{\mathbf{C}} = \frac{2\mathbf{X}_1\mathbf{X}_2}{\mathbf{X}_2-\mathbf{X}_1} \cdot \frac{\mathbf{X}_2-\mathbf{X}_1}{2} = \mathbf{X}_1\mathbf{X}_2$$

$$\therefore \mathbf{Z_0} = \sqrt{\mathbf{X}_1\mathbf{X}_2}\ \Omega$$

Now $\quad \varepsilon^\gamma = \dfrac{\mathbf{I_S}}{\mathbf{I_R}} = \dfrac{\mathbf{CV_R}+\mathbf{DI_R}}{\mathbf{I_R}} = \dfrac{\mathbf{CI_R Z_0}+\mathbf{DI_R}}{\mathbf{I_R}}$

$$= \mathbf{CZ_0}+\mathbf{D}$$

$$= \frac{2}{\mathbf{X}_2-\mathbf{X}_1} \cdot \mathbf{Z_0} + \frac{\mathbf{X}_2+\mathbf{X}_1}{\mathbf{X}_2-\mathbf{X}_1}$$

$$= \frac{2\mathbf{Z_0}+\mathbf{X}_2+\mathbf{X}_1}{\mathbf{X}_2-\mathbf{X}_1}$$

$$\therefore \frac{\varepsilon^\gamma-1}{\varepsilon^\gamma+1} = \frac{2\mathbf{Z_0}+2\mathbf{X}_1}{2\mathbf{Z_0}+2\mathbf{X}_2}$$

$$= \frac{\sqrt{\mathbf{X}_1\mathbf{X}_2}+\mathbf{X}_1}{\sqrt{\mathbf{X}_1\mathbf{X}_2}+\mathbf{X}_2}$$

$$= \sqrt{\frac{\mathbf{X}_1}{\mathbf{X}_2}} \cdot \left(\frac{\sqrt{\mathbf{X}_2}+\sqrt{\mathbf{X}_1}}{\sqrt{\mathbf{X}_1}+\sqrt{\mathbf{X}_2}}\right)$$

$$= \sqrt{\frac{\mathbf{X}_1}{\mathbf{X}_2}} = \tanh\frac{\gamma}{2}$$

Let $\mathbf{X}_1 = -jX_1$ and $\mathbf{X}_2 = +jX_2$

$$\therefore \tanh\frac{\gamma}{2} = \sqrt{\frac{-X_1}{X_2}} = j\sqrt{\frac{X_1}{X_2}}$$

$\therefore \gamma = 2\tanh^{-1} j\sqrt{X_1/X_2}$ which must be of the form $0+j\beta$

If $$\mathbf{X}_1 = +jX_1 \quad \text{and} \quad \mathbf{X}_2 = -jX_2$$

$$\tanh\frac{\gamma}{2} = \sqrt{\frac{-X_1}{X_2}} = j\sqrt{\frac{X_1}{X_2}}$$

$$\therefore \text{ again } \gamma = 2\tanh^{-1} j\sqrt{X_1/X_2} = 0+j\beta$$

Since γ is imaginary, if $\mathbf{X}_1$ and $\mathbf{X}_2$ are of opposite sign, $\alpha = 0$; hence, there will be zero attenuation at all frequencies.

2. Explain what is meant by (*a*) a travelling wave and (*b*) a standing wave on a transmission line.

Two long transmission lines with different characteristic impedances are connected together. Derive expressions for the reflection and transmission coefficients for voltage and current.

A cable with a characteristic impedance of 80 Ω is joined in series with an open-wire line having a characteristic impedance of 700 Ω. If, as a consequence of connecting a direct voltage to the cable, a steep-fronted voltage of 1·2 kV travels along it, determine the voltage and current in the cable and open-wire line immediately after the travelling wave has reached the junction. Assume the lines to be loss free.

Solution For the definitions of travelling and standing wave see Paper No. VI—June, 1962, question No. 6, page 90.

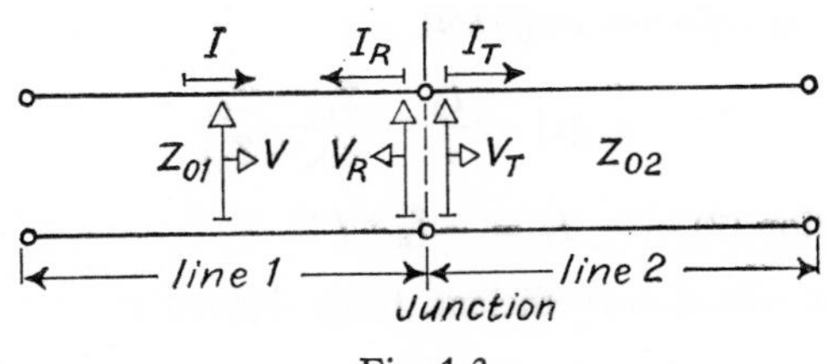

Fig. 1.3

Let V and I be the magnitudes of the incident voltage and current respectively; V_R and I_R are the magnitudes of the voltage and current, respectively, reflected at the junction of the two lines; V_T and I_T are the magnitudes of the voltage and current, respectively, transmitted beyond the junction of the two lines.

Assume, since the transmission lines are long, that there are no reflections from the termination of line 2.

$\therefore$ The voltage in line 1 at the junction

= The voltage in line 2 at the junction

$$\therefore V+V_R = V_T \qquad (1)$$

Applying Kirchhoff's first law at the junction,

$$I = I_R + I_T \tag{2}$$

Also $$\frac{V}{I} = Z_{01}; \quad \frac{V_R}{I_R} = Z_{01}; \quad \frac{V_T}{I_T} = Z_{02}$$

∴ from equation (2),

$$\frac{V}{Z_{01}} = \frac{V_R}{Z_{01}} + \frac{V_T}{Z_{02}}$$

$$\therefore V\frac{Z_{02}}{Z_{01}} = V_R\frac{Z_{02}}{Z_{01}} + V_T \tag{3}$$

Subtracting equation (1) from equation (3),

$$V\left(\frac{Z_{02}}{Z_{01}} - 1\right) = V_R\left(\frac{Z_{02}}{Z_{01}} + 1\right)$$

∴ *The voltage reflection coefficient*

$$= |\rho_v| = \frac{V_R}{V} = \frac{Z_{02} - Z_{01}}{Z_{02} + Z_{01}}$$

Now $$\frac{V_R}{V} = \frac{I_R Z_{01}}{I Z_{01}} = \frac{Z_{02} - Z_{01}}{Z_{02} + Z_{01}}$$

∴ *The current reflection coefficient*

$$= |\rho_i| = \frac{I_R}{I} = \frac{Z_{02} - Z_{01}}{Z_{02} + Z_{01}}$$

From equation (2), $I_T = -I_R + I$

∴ the current reflection coefficient, being defined as

$$\frac{\text{reflected current}}{\text{incident current}} = -\frac{I_R}{I} = -|\rho_i|$$

$$\therefore \rho_i = \frac{Z_{01} - Z_{02}}{Z_{02} + Z_{01}}$$ Note: $\rho_v = -\rho_i$

The voltage transmission coefficient

$$= \frac{V + V_R}{V} = 1 + |\rho_v| = \frac{2Z_{02}}{Z_{02} + Z_{01}} \tag{4}$$

The current transmission coefficient

$$= \frac{I - I_R}{I} = 1 - |\rho_i| = \frac{2Z_{01}}{Z_{02} + Z_{01}} \tag{5}$$

Numerical portion

Given $Z_{01} = 80\ \Omega$; $Z_{02} = 700\ \Omega$; $V = 1200$ V

The voltage in the cable and the open-wire line immediately after the travelling wave has reached the junction is given by equation (4);

$$V+V_R = \frac{2Z_{02}}{Z_{02}+Z_{01}} \cdot V = \frac{2\times 700}{780} \times 1{\cdot}2 \text{ kV} = \underline{2{\cdot}154 \text{ kV}}$$

The current in the cable and the open-wire line immediately after the travelling wave has reached the junction is given by equation (5):

$$I-I_R = \frac{2Z_{01}}{Z_{02}+Z_{01}} \cdot \frac{V}{Z_{01}} = \frac{2\times 1200}{780} = \underline{3{\cdot}08 \text{ A}}$$

3. Draw the general circuit arrangement of a 4-arm a.c. bridge suitable for the measurement of the capacitance and loss angle of a capacitor. Derive the balance equation of the bridge and obtain an expression for the loss angle of the unknown capacitor in terms of the other components. Draw the vector diagram for the bridge in the balanced position.

Solution

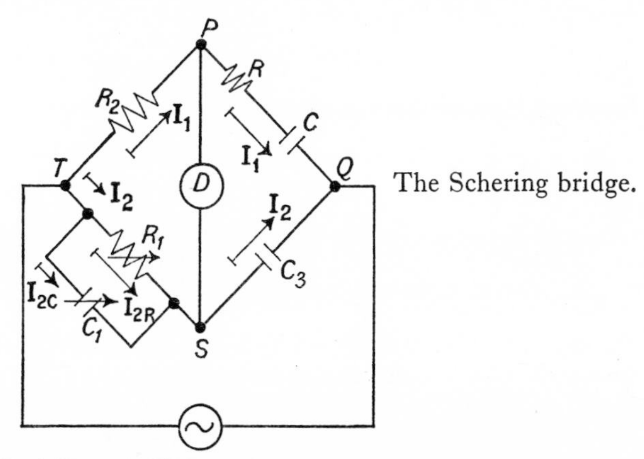

Fig. 1.4—4-arm a.c. bridge suitable for the measurement of capacitance and loss-angle of a capacitor

C is the unknown capacitor under test, the losses being represented by the resistor R
R_2 is a standard non-inducive resistor
C_3 is a standard loss-free capacitor
C_1 is a standard loss-free variable capacitor
R_1 is a standard non-inductive variable resistor
D is a high impedance detector

Evidently at balance:

$$\mathbf{V_{TP}} = \mathbf{V_{TS}} \quad \text{and} \quad \mathbf{V_{PQ}} = \mathbf{V_{SQ}}$$

$$\therefore \mathbf{I}_1 \cdot \mathbf{Z_{TP}} = \mathbf{I}_2 \cdot \mathbf{Z_{TS}}$$

and

$$\mathbf{I}_1 \cdot \mathbf{Z_{PQ}} = \mathbf{I}_2 \cdot \mathbf{Z_{SQ}}$$

$$\therefore \mathbf{Z_{TP}} \cdot \mathbf{Z_{SQ}} = \mathbf{Z_{TS}} \cdot \mathbf{Z_{PQ}}$$

$$\therefore R_2 \cdot \left(\frac{-j}{\omega C_3}\right) = \frac{R_1\left(\dfrac{-j}{\omega C_1}\right)}{R_1 - \dfrac{j}{\omega C_1}} \cdot \left(R - \frac{j}{\omega C}\right)$$

$$\therefore R_2\left(\frac{-j}{\omega C_3}\right)\left(R_1 - \frac{j}{\omega C_1}\right) = R_1\left(\frac{-j}{\omega C_1}\right)\left(R - \frac{j}{\omega C}\right)$$

$$\therefore = -j\frac{R_1 R_2}{\omega C_3} - \frac{R_2}{\omega^2 C_1 C_3} = -j\frac{R_1 R}{\omega C_1} - \frac{R_1}{\omega^2 C C_1}$$

Equating in phase component:

$$\frac{R_2}{\omega^2 C_1 C_3} = \frac{R_1}{\omega^2 C C_1}$$

$$\therefore C = \frac{R_1}{R_2} \cdot C_3 \tag{1}$$

Equating in quadrature component:

$$\frac{R_1 R_2}{\omega C_3} = \frac{R_1 R}{\omega C_1}$$

$$\therefore R = \frac{C_1}{C_3} \cdot R_2 \tag{2}$$

Both equations (1) and (2) must be satisfied at balance. The losses of the capacitor C is represented by a series resistor R, but it may also be represented by a high value shunt resistor.

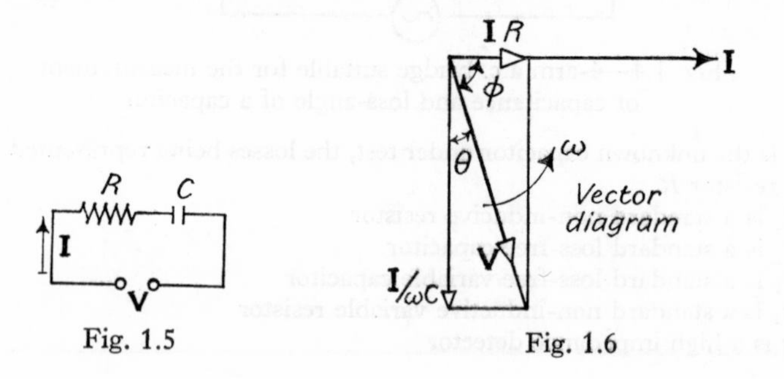

Fig. 1.5

Fig. 1.6

$$\text{Loss angle} = \text{power factor} = \cos\phi = \sin\theta$$

$$= \tan\theta \quad \text{since } \theta \text{ is small}$$

$$= \frac{IR}{I/\omega C} = \omega CR$$

$$= \omega\frac{R_1}{R_2}\cdot C_3\cdot\frac{C_1}{C_3}\cdot R_2$$

$$= \underline{\omega C_1 R_1}$$

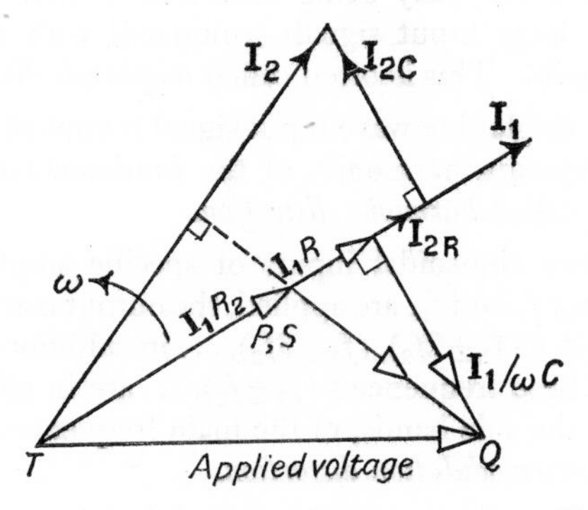

Fig. 1.7—Vector diagram of the Schering bridge at balance

4. Discuss the cause and effects of non-linearity in amplifiers.

The output current/input voltage characteristic of an amplifier with a resistive load may be represented by the relation

$$I = a+bV+cV^2$$

Deduce the ratio of the second-harmonic component in the output to the fundamental.

The application of a sinusoidal input voltage to an amplifier causes the output current to vary between the limits of 180% and 45% of the value with no input voltage. Determine the percentage second harmonic in the output current.

Solution Cause of non-linearity in amplifiers

1. It may be shown that the anode current of a triode valve is $I_a = K(V_g+V_a/\mu)^{3/2}$, where K is a constant determined by the geometry of the valve, V_g, V_a, and μ have the usual conventional meanings. It is evident that this equation is non-linear. A similar condition holds for pentode valves. It is evident that the main cause of non-linearity is due

to the eccentricity of the electrodes in the physical construction of the valve.

2. With large signal inputs to an amplifier, grid current may flow, causing an effective decrease in anode current.

3. Secondary emission from the anode of a valve may give rise to a space charge region, which prevents the further flow of space current in a valve.

The effects of non-linearity in amplifiers

1. A variation in gain of the amplifier with the amplitude of the input signal, the gain normally being measured in decibels. There may be less gain for large input signals, compared with the small amplitude input signal gain. This is often called *amplitude distortion.*

2. When a single sine wave input signal is applied to the amplifier, the output may contain harmonics of the fundamental applied frequency. This is often called *harmonic distortion.*

3. When two sinusoidal inputs of specific amplitudes, and specific frequencies, say f_1 and f_2, are applied, the output may contain frequencies such as $(f_1 \pm f_2)$, $(f_1 \pm 2f_2)$, $(f_1 \pm 3f_2)$, ... in addition to the frequencies f_1 and f_2. These frequencies $(f_1 \pm f_2)$, ... are in effect side bands, and harmonics of the side bands, of the main frequencies f_1 and f_2. This is often called *intermodulation distortion.*

Note: The above is not an exhaustive solution, but an indication of the type of answer expected in the limited examination time available. It is left to the reader to think of other causes of non-linearity in amplifiers, with special reference to, say, transistor amplifiers.

Let the input signal $V = V_m \sin \omega t$

Now $$I = a + bV + cV^2$$

$$= a + bV_m \sin \omega t + cV_m^2 \sin^2 \omega t \tag{1}$$

$$= a + bV_m \sin \omega t + \frac{cV_m^2}{2}(1 - \cos 2\omega t)$$

$$= \left(a + \frac{cV_m^2}{2}\right) + bV_m \sin \omega t - \frac{cV_m^2}{2} \cos 2\omega t$$

$$= \text{d.c. term} + \text{fundamental} - \text{second harmonic}$$

$\therefore$ amplitude of the fundamental $= bV_m$

amplitude of the second harmonic $= cV_m^2/2$

$$\therefore \frac{\text{second harmonic component in the output}}{\text{fundamental component in the output}}$$

$$= \frac{cV_m^2}{2} \cdot \frac{1}{bV_m} = \frac{cV_m}{2b} \quad \textit{Ans.}$$

With no input voltage $\omega t = 0$. Therefore from equation (1) the output current $I_o = a =$ the d.c. term.

For maximum output $\qquad \omega t = \pi/2$

$$\therefore I = a + bV_m + cV_m^2 = \hat{I} \tag{2}$$

For minimum output $\qquad \omega t = 3\pi/2$

$$\therefore I = a - bV_m + cV_m^2 = \check{I} \tag{3}$$

Adding equations (2) and (3) gives

$$\hat{I} + \check{I} = 2a + 2cV_m^2$$

$$\text{Amplitude of second harmonic} = cV_m^2/2 = \frac{\hat{I} + \check{I} - 2a}{4} \tag{4}$$

Subtracting equation (3) from equation (2) gives

$$\hat{I} - \check{I} = 2bV_m$$

$$\text{Amplitude of fundamental} = bV_m = \frac{\hat{I} - \check{I}}{2} \tag{5}$$

$\therefore$ from equations (4) and (5):

Percentage second harmonic in the output current:

$$= \frac{\hat{I} + \check{I} - 2I_0}{2(\hat{I} - \check{I})} \times 100\%$$

$$= \frac{1 \cdot 8I_0 + 0 \cdot 45I_0 - 2I_0}{2(1 \cdot 8I_0 - 0 \cdot 45I_0)} \times 100\%$$

since $\hat{I} = 1{\cdot}8I_0$, given and $\check{I} = 0{\cdot}45I_0$, given

$= 9{\cdot}26\%$ *Ans.*

5. Three voltmeters having resistances of 10, 10, and 5 kΩ, respectively, are connected in star to a balanced 3-phase, 3-wire supply. The line voltage is 440 V. Determine the readings of the three voltmeters.

Solution

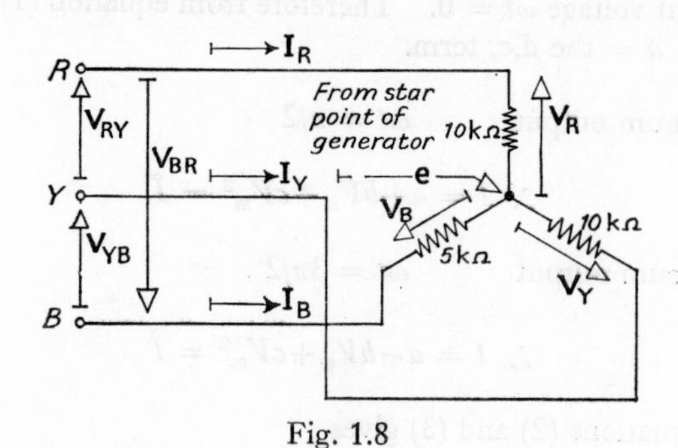

Fig. 1.8

1. Using the conventional directions of voltage and current as illustrated in the circuit diagram,
2. assuming phase sequence RYB,
3. using the red phase generator voltage as a reference vector, then

$$\mathbf{E_R} = E(1+j0)$$

$$\mathbf{E_Y} = a^2\mathbf{E_R} = a^2E$$

$$\mathbf{E_B} = a\mathbf{E_R} = aE$$

Now
$$\mathbf{I_R} = \frac{\mathbf{V_R}}{10^4} = \frac{\mathbf{E_R}-\mathbf{e}}{10^4} = \frac{E-\mathbf{e}}{10^4}\ A$$

and
$$\mathbf{I_Y} = \frac{\mathbf{V_Y}}{10^4} = \frac{a^2\mathbf{E_R}-\mathbf{e}}{10^4} = \frac{a^2E-\mathbf{e}}{10^4}\ A$$

and
$$\mathbf{I_B} = \frac{\mathbf{V_B}}{5.10^3} = \frac{a\mathbf{E_R}-\mathbf{e}}{5.10^3} = \frac{aE-\mathbf{e}}{5.10^3}\ A$$

Now since the system is 3-phase, 3-wire,

$$\mathbf{I_R}+\mathbf{I_Y}+\mathbf{I_B} = 0$$

$$\therefore \quad \frac{E-\mathbf{e}}{10^4}+\frac{a^2E-\mathbf{e}}{10^4}+\frac{aE-\mathbf{e}}{5.10^3} = 0$$

$$\therefore\ \mathbf{e} = \frac{E}{4}(1+a^2+2a)$$

$$= \frac{aE}{4} \quad \text{since } 1+a+a^2 = 0$$

$$\therefore\ \mathbf{V_R} = E\left(1-\frac{a}{4}\right) = \frac{E}{4}(4-a)$$

$$= \frac{440}{\sqrt{3}}\cdot\frac{1}{4}\left(\frac{9}{2}-j\frac{\sqrt{3}}{2}\right)$$

$$= \frac{55}{\sqrt{3}}(9-j\sqrt{3})$$

∴ The voltmeters having resistances of 10 kΩ read

$$|\mathbf{V_R}| = |\mathbf{V_Y}| = \frac{55}{\sqrt{3}}\cdot\sqrt{84} = \underline{292\text{ V}} \quad \textit{Ans.}$$

Now $$\mathbf{V_B} = E\left(a-\frac{a}{4}\right) = \frac{3aE}{4} = \frac{3}{4}\cdot\frac{440}{\sqrt{3}}\cdot\left(-\frac{1}{2}+j\frac{\sqrt{3}}{2}\right)$$

∴ The voltmeter having a resistance of 5 kΩ reads

$$|\mathbf{V_B}| = \frac{330}{\sqrt{3}} = \underline{191\text{ V}} \quad \textit{Ans.}$$

6. A 3-phase star-connected alternator, with the star point solidly earthed, is short-circuited

(*a*) between one line terminal and earth,

(*b*) by the two line terminals being simultaneously connected to earth.

Derive for each case an expression for the sustained short-circuit in terms of the alternator voltage and the symmetrical-component impedances of the machine.

Solution (*a*) *Short-circuit between one line terminal and earth*

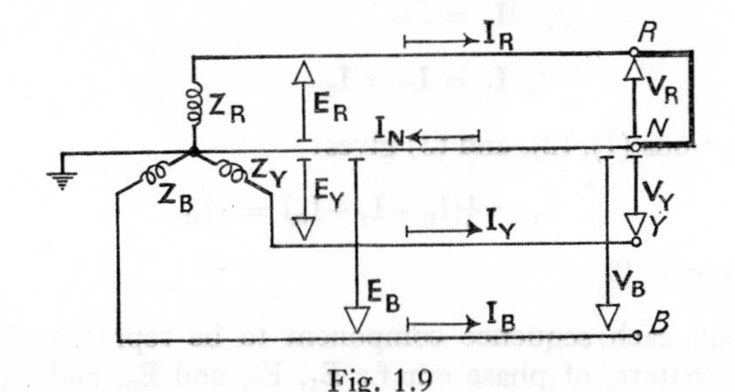

Fig. 1.9

Let the phase sequence be RYB; the respective alternator phase e.m.f.s under open circuit conditions

$$\mathbf{E_R} = E(1+j0), \text{ the reference vector}$$

$$\therefore \mathbf{E_Y} = a^2E = \left(-\frac{1}{2}-j\frac{\sqrt{3}}{2}\right)E$$

$$\text{and } \mathbf{E_B} = aE = \left(-\frac{1}{2}+j\frac{\sqrt{3}}{2}\right)E$$

Let the alternator have impedance:

$\mathbf{Z}_1$ to the positive phase sequence component of current
$\mathbf{Z}_2$ to the negative phase sequence component of current
$\mathbf{Z}_0$ to the zero sequence component of current

Now it is known that

$$\mathbf{I_R} = \mathbf{I}_1+\mathbf{I}_2+\mathbf{I}_0 \quad (1)$$

$$\mathbf{I_Y} = a^2\mathbf{I}_1+a\mathbf{I}_2+\mathbf{I}_0 \quad (2)$$

$$\mathbf{I_B} = a\mathbf{I}_1+a^2\mathbf{I}_2+\mathbf{I}_0 \quad (3)$$

where $\mathbf{I}_1$, $\mathbf{I}_2$, and $\mathbf{I}_0$ are the positive phase sequence, negative phase sequence, and zero sequence components of currents, respectively.

Now since $\mathbf{I_Y} = \mathbf{I_B} = 0$, then from equations (2) and (3)

$$a^2\mathbf{I}_1+a\mathbf{I}_2+\mathbf{I}_0 = a\mathbf{I}_1+a^2\mathbf{I}_2+\mathbf{I}_0$$

$$\therefore \mathbf{I}_1(a^2-a) = \mathbf{I}_2(a^2-a)$$

$$\therefore \mathbf{I}_1 = \mathbf{I}_2 \quad (4)$$

From equation (1)

$$\mathbf{I_R} = \mathbf{I}_1+\mathbf{I}_2+\mathbf{I}_0 = 3\mathbf{I}_0$$

$$\therefore 2\mathbf{I}_1 = 2\mathbf{I}_0$$

$$\therefore \mathbf{I}_1 = \mathbf{I}_2 = \mathbf{I}_0 \quad (5)$$

Adding equations (1), (2), and (3) gives:

$$\mathbf{I}_0 = \tfrac{1}{3}[\mathbf{I_R}+\mathbf{I_Y}+\mathbf{I_B}] = \tfrac{1}{3}\mathbf{I_R} \quad (6)$$

since $1+a+a^2 = 0$.

Considering each sequence component to be represented by three separate alternators, of phase e.m.f.s $\mathbf{E}_1$, $\mathbf{E}_2$, and $\mathbf{E}_0$, and having load voltages $\mathbf{V}_1$, $\mathbf{V}_2$, and $\mathbf{V}_0$; the suffices 1, 2, 0, representing postive phase sequence, negative phase sequence, and zero sequence components, respectively, then by Kirchhoff's second law:

$$\mathbf{E}_1 = \mathbf{I}_1\mathbf{Z}_1+\mathbf{V}_1 \tag{7}$$

$$\mathbf{E}_2 = \mathbf{I}_2\mathbf{Z}_2+\mathbf{V}_2 \tag{8}$$

$$\mathbf{E}_0 = \mathbf{I}_0\mathbf{Z}_0+\mathbf{V}_0 \tag{9}$$

Since the alternator e.m.f. is balanced, $\mathbf{E}_1 = E_1 \quad \mathbf{E}_2 = 0, \quad \mathbf{E}_0 = 0.$

$\therefore$ Adding equations (7), (8), and (9),

$$\mathbf{E}_1 = E = \mathbf{I}_1\mathbf{Z}_1+\mathbf{I}_2\mathbf{Z}_2+\mathbf{I}_0\mathbf{Z}_0$$

Since $\mathbf{V_R} = \mathbf{V}_1+\mathbf{V}_2+\mathbf{V}_0 = 0 =$ the red phase load voltage.

$$\therefore\ E = \mathbf{I}_0(\mathbf{Z}_1+\mathbf{Z}_2+\mathbf{Z}_0) = \tfrac{1}{3}\mathbf{I_R}(\mathbf{Z}_1+\mathbf{Z}_2+\mathbf{Z}_0)$$

The fault current is

$$\mathbf{I_R} = \frac{3E}{(\mathbf{Z}_1+\mathbf{Z}_2+\mathbf{Z}_0)}\ A \quad \textit{Ans.}$$

(*b*) *Short-circuit between the two line terminals, being simultaneously connected to earth.*

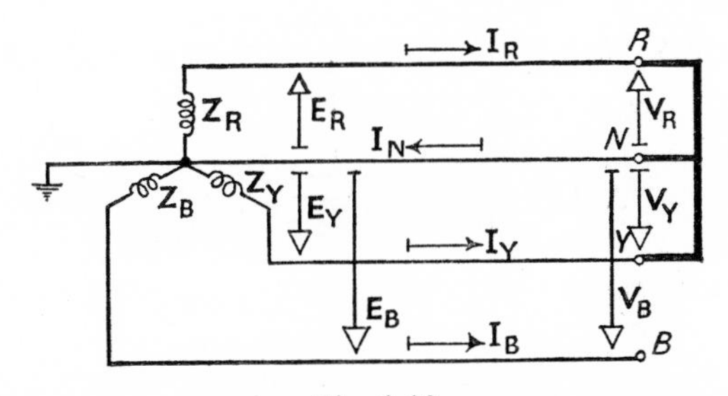

Fig. 1.10

Evidently $\qquad \mathbf{V_R} = \mathbf{V_Y} = 0 \quad \text{and} \quad \mathbf{I_B} = 0$

Using the same definitions as in section (*a*) then

$$\mathbf{I_R} = \mathbf{I}_1+\mathbf{I}_2+\mathbf{I}_0 \tag{1}$$

$$\mathbf{I_Y} = a^2\mathbf{I}_1+a\mathbf{I}_2+\mathbf{I}_0 \tag{2}$$

$$\mathbf{I_B} = a\mathbf{I}_1+a^2\mathbf{I}_2+\mathbf{I}_0 = 0 \tag{3}$$

Also applying Kirchhoff's second law to each phase,

$$\mathbf{V_R} = \mathbf{E_R} - \mathbf{I}_0\mathbf{Z}_0 - \mathbf{I}_1\mathbf{Z}_1 - \mathbf{I}_2\mathbf{Z}_2 = 0 \tag{4}$$

$$\mathbf{V_Y} = \mathbf{E_Y} - \mathbf{I}_0\mathbf{Z}_0 - a^2\mathbf{I}_1\mathbf{Z}_1 - a\mathbf{I}_2\mathbf{Z}_2 = 0 \tag{5}$$

$$\mathbf{V_B} = \mathbf{E_B} - \mathbf{I}_0\mathbf{Z}_0 - a\mathbf{I}_1\mathbf{Z}_1 - a^2\mathbf{I}_2\mathbf{Z}_2 \tag{6}$$

From equations (3), (4), and (5),

$$1\mathbf{I}_0 + a^2\mathbf{I}_2 + a\mathbf{I}_1 = 0 \tag{7}$$

$$\mathbf{Z}_0\mathbf{I}_0 + \mathbf{Z}_2\mathbf{I}_2 + \mathbf{Z}_1\mathbf{I}_1 = E \tag{8}$$

$$\mathbf{Z}_0\mathbf{I}_0 + a\mathbf{Z}_2\mathbf{I}_2 + a^2\mathbf{Z}_1\mathbf{I}_1 = a^2E \tag{9}$$

Solving equations (7), (8), and (9) by means of determinants,

$$\mathbf{I}_0 = \frac{\begin{vmatrix} 0 & a^2 & a \\ E & \mathbf{Z}_2 & \mathbf{Z}_1 \\ a^2E & a\mathbf{Z}_2 & a^2\mathbf{Z}_1 \end{vmatrix}}{\begin{vmatrix} 1 & a^2 & a \\ \mathbf{Z}_0 & \mathbf{Z}_2 & \mathbf{Z}_1 \\ \mathbf{Z}_0 & a\mathbf{Z}_2 & a^2\mathbf{Z}_1 \end{vmatrix}} = \frac{\Delta_1}{\Delta}$$

$$\therefore \Delta_1 = -a^2(Ea^2\mathbf{Z}_1 - a^2E\mathbf{Z}_1) + a(Ea\mathbf{Z}_2 - a^2E\mathbf{Z}_2)$$

$$= E\mathbf{Z}_2(a^2-1) \quad \text{since } a^3 = 1$$

$$\text{and } \Delta = 1(a^2\mathbf{Z}_1\mathbf{Z}_2 - a\mathbf{Z}_1\mathbf{Z}_2) - a^2(a^2\mathbf{Z}_0\mathbf{Z}_1 - \mathbf{Z}_0\mathbf{Z}_1) + a(a\mathbf{Z}_0\mathbf{Z}_2 - \mathbf{Z}_0\mathbf{Z}_2)$$

$$= (a^2-a)(\mathbf{Z}_1\mathbf{Z}_2 + \mathbf{Z}_0\mathbf{Z}_1 + \mathbf{Z}_0\mathbf{Z}_2)$$

$$\therefore \mathbf{I}_0 = \frac{(a^2-1)E\mathbf{Z}_2}{(a^2-a)(\mathbf{Z}_1\mathbf{Z}_2 + \mathbf{Z}_0\mathbf{Z}_1 + \mathbf{Z}_0\mathbf{Z}_2)}$$

$$\text{Now } \frac{a^2-1}{a^2-a} = \frac{(a-1)(a+1)}{a(a-1)} = \frac{-a^2}{a} = -a, \text{ since } a^2+a+1 = 0$$

$$\therefore \mathbf{I}_0 = \frac{-aE\mathbf{Z}_2}{\mathbf{Z}_1\mathbf{Z}_2 + \mathbf{Z}_0\mathbf{Z}_1 + \mathbf{Z}_0\mathbf{Z}_2} \tag{10}$$

and

$$\mathbf{I}_2 = \frac{\begin{vmatrix} 1 & 0 & a \\ \mathbf{Z}_0 & E & \mathbf{Z}_1 \\ \mathbf{Z}_0 & a^2E & a^2\mathbf{Z}_1 \end{vmatrix}}{\Delta} = \frac{\Delta_2}{\Delta}$$

$$\therefore \Delta_2 = (a^2E\mathbf{Z}_1 - a^2E\mathbf{Z}_1) + a(a^2E\mathbf{Z}_0 - E\mathbf{Z}_0)$$

$$= a(a^2-1)E\mathbf{Z}_0$$

Now $\dfrac{a(a^2-1)}{a^2-a} = \dfrac{a(a-1)(a+1)}{a(a-1)} = a+1 = -a^2$

$$\therefore\ \mathbf{I}_2 = \frac{-a^2E\mathbf{Z}_0}{\mathbf{Z}_1\mathbf{Z}_2+\mathbf{Z}_0\mathbf{Z}_1+\mathbf{Z}_0\mathbf{Z}_2} \tag{11}$$

$$\mathbf{I}_1 = \frac{\begin{vmatrix} 1 & a^2 & 0 \\ \mathbf{Z}_0 & \mathbf{Z}_2 & E \\ \mathbf{Z}_0 & a\mathbf{Z}_2 & a^2E \end{vmatrix}}{\Delta} = \frac{\Delta_1}{\Delta}$$

$$\therefore\ \Delta_1 = (a^2E\mathbf{Z}_2 - aE\mathbf{Z}_2) - a^2(a^2E\mathbf{Z}_0 - E\mathbf{Z}_0)$$

$$= (a^2-a)E(\mathbf{Z}_0+\mathbf{Z}_2) \quad \text{since } a^4 = a^3.a = a$$

$$\therefore\ \mathbf{I}_1 = \frac{E(\mathbf{Z}_0+\mathbf{Z}_2)}{\mathbf{Z}_1\mathbf{Z}_2+\mathbf{Z}_0\mathbf{Z}_1+\mathbf{Z}_0\mathbf{Z}_2} \tag{12}$$

Now, from equations (1), (10), (11), and (12), the sustained short-cuit current in the red line

$$= \mathbf{I}_R = \frac{E(\mathbf{Z}_0+\mathbf{Z}_2) - a^2E\mathbf{Z}_0 - aE\mathbf{Z}_2}{\mathbf{Z}_1\mathbf{Z}_2+\mathbf{Z}_0\mathbf{Z}_1+\mathbf{Z}_0\mathbf{Z}_2}$$

$$= \frac{E\mathbf{Z}_0(1-a^2)+E\mathbf{Z}_2(1-a)}{\mathbf{Z}_1\mathbf{Z}_2+\mathbf{Z}_0\mathbf{Z}_1+\mathbf{Z}_0\mathbf{Z}_2}\ \text{A} \tag{13}$$

Also from equations (2), (10), (11), and (12) the sustained short-circuit current in the yellow line

$$= \mathbf{I}_Y = \frac{a^2E(\mathbf{Z}_0+\mathbf{Z}_2) - a^3E\mathbf{Z}_0 - aE\mathbf{Z}_2}{\mathbf{Z}_1\mathbf{Z}_2+\mathbf{Z}_0\mathbf{Z}_1+\mathbf{Z}_0\mathbf{Z}_2}$$

$$= \frac{E\mathbf{Z}_0(a^2-1)+E\mathbf{Z}_2(a^2-a)}{\mathbf{Z}_1\mathbf{Z}_2+\mathbf{Z}_0\mathbf{Z}_1+\mathbf{Z}_0\mathbf{Z}_2}\ \text{A} \quad \textit{Ans.} \tag{14}$$

The total sustained short-circuit current flowing to earth

$$= \mathbf{I}_N = \mathbf{I}_R + \mathbf{I}_Y$$

$$= \frac{-3aE\mathbf{Z}_2}{\mathbf{Z}_1\mathbf{Z}_2+\mathbf{Z}_0\mathbf{Z}_1+\mathbf{Z}_0\mathbf{Z}_2}\ \text{A} \quad \textit{Ans.}$$

since $1-a+a^2-a = -3a$.

7. A closed-loop electrical servo-mechanism is used to control the angular position of a rotatable mass in response to the rotation of a control handle. The rotation of the mass is subject to viscous damping. Draw a block diagram for a suitable scheme and set up the differential equation of the system.

In a particular case, where a mass is required to follow the movement of a control handle, the moment of inertia of the moving parts, referred to the mass under control, is 200 kg-m². The driving torque, also referred to the mass, is 30 newton-metres per minute of misalignment. If the system is critically damped, calculate the steady-state angular error when the control handle is continuously rotated at 1 rev/min.

Solution For the block diagram see Paper No. III—November 1960, question No. 6, page 43. For the definition of terms, and proof of the differential equation, see Paper No. IV—June 1961, question No. 7, page 61.

Now
$$J\frac{d^2\theta_o}{dt^2}+F\frac{d\theta_o}{dt}+K\theta_o = K\theta_i$$

$$\therefore \frac{d^2\theta_o}{dt^2}+\frac{F}{J}\cdot\frac{d\theta_o}{dt} = \frac{K}{J}(\theta_i-\theta_o)$$

and $\omega_n^2 = K/J$

$$\therefore \frac{1}{\omega_n^2}\cdot\frac{d^2\theta_o}{dt^2}+T\frac{d\theta_o}{dt} = (\theta_i-\theta_o)$$

In the steady-state condition, the output shaft has ceased to accelerate, and the input and output shafts rotate at constant velocity.

$$\therefore (\theta_i-\theta_o) = T\frac{d\theta_o}{dt} = T\frac{d\theta_i}{dt}$$

If the system is critically damped, $\omega_n T = 2$

$$\therefore T = \frac{2}{\omega_n} = \frac{2}{\sqrt{K/J}} = 2\sqrt{\frac{J}{K}}\text{ sec}$$

Now
$$J = 200 \text{ kg-m}^2,$$

$$\frac{d\theta_i}{dt} = 1 \text{ rev/min} = \frac{2\pi}{60}\text{ rad/s},$$

$$K = 30\times 60\times\frac{180}{\pi}\text{ Nm/radian}$$

$$\therefore\ (\theta_i - \theta_o) = 2\sqrt{\frac{200\pi}{180\times 30\times 60}}\times\frac{\pi}{30}$$

$$= 0{\cdot}0092 \text{ rad}$$

$$= \frac{0{\cdot}0092\times 180°}{\pi}$$

$$= \underline{0{\cdot}53°} \quad \textit{Ans.}$$

= the steady state angular error,
sometimes called the velocity lag.

PAPER NO. II—JUNE 1960

1. A transmission circuit is represented by a symmetrical π-network in which the series impedance is $120\angle 60°$ ohms, and each shunt admittance is $2{\cdot}5\times 10^{-3}\angle 90°$ mho. Calculate (*a*) the value of the general circuit constants A *B C D*, and (*b*) the characteristic impedance of the circuit.

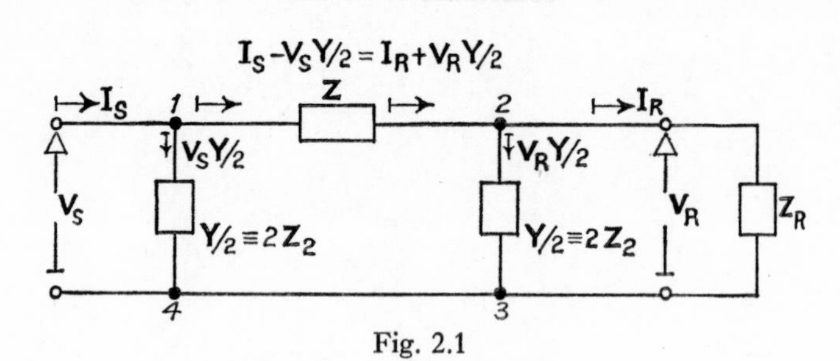

Fig. 2.1

Solution Applying Kirchhoff's second law to the closed mesh 1 2 3 4,

$$\mathbf{V_S} = \left(\mathbf{I_R}+\mathbf{V_R}\frac{\mathbf{Y}}{2}\right)\mathbf{Z}+\mathbf{V_R}$$

$$= \left(1+\frac{\mathbf{YZ}}{2}\right)\mathbf{V_R}+\mathbf{ZI_R}$$

Compare $\mathbf{V_S} = \mathbf{AV_R}+\mathbf{BI_R}$, the general circuit equation.

$\therefore$ comparing coefficients of $\mathbf{V_R}$ and $\mathbf{I_R}$

$$\mathbf{A} = \left(1+\frac{\mathbf{YZ}}{2}\right) \quad \text{and} \quad \mathbf{B} = \mathbf{Z}$$

$$\therefore \mathbf{B} = 120\angle 60° = 120\left(\frac{1}{2}+j\frac{\sqrt{3}}{2}\right) = 60(1+j\sqrt{3})\ \Omega \quad \textit{Ans.}$$

$$\therefore \mathbf{A} = 1+120\angle 60°\times 2{\cdot}5\,.\,10^{-3}\angle 90°$$

$$= 1+0{\cdot}3\angle 150°$$

$$= 1+0{\cdot}3\left(-\frac{\sqrt{3}}{2}+j\frac{1}{2}\right)$$

$$= 0{\cdot}7402+j0{\cdot}150 \quad \textit{Ans.}$$

Also applying Kirchhoff's second law again to the closed mesh 1 2 3 4

$$\mathbf{V_S} = \left(\mathbf{I_S} - \mathbf{V_S}\frac{\mathbf{Y}}{2}\right)\mathbf{Z} + \mathbf{V_R}$$

$$= \mathbf{I_S Z} - \mathbf{V_S}\frac{\mathbf{YZ}}{2} + \mathbf{V_R}$$

$$\therefore \mathbf{I_S Z} = \mathbf{V_S}\left(1 + \frac{\mathbf{YZ}}{2}\right) - \mathbf{V_R}$$

$$= \left[\left(1 + \frac{\mathbf{YZ}}{2}\right)\mathbf{V_R} + \mathbf{ZI_R}\right]\left(1 + \frac{\mathbf{YZ}}{2}\right) - \mathbf{V_R}$$

$$= \mathbf{YZ}\left(1 + \frac{\mathbf{YZ}}{4}\right)\mathbf{V_R} + \mathbf{Z}\left(1 + \frac{\mathbf{YZ}}{2}\right)\mathbf{I_R}$$

$$\therefore \mathbf{I_S} = \mathbf{Y}\left(1 + \frac{\mathbf{YZ}}{4}\right)\mathbf{V_R} + \left(1 + \frac{\mathbf{YZ}}{2}\right)\mathbf{I_R}$$

Compare $\mathbf{I_S} = \mathbf{CV_R} + \mathbf{DI_R}$, the general circuit equation

$\therefore$ comparing coefficients of $\mathbf{V_R}$ and $\mathbf{I_R}$

$$\mathbf{C} = \mathbf{Y}\left(1 + \frac{\mathbf{YZ}}{4}\right)$$

and $$\mathbf{D} = \mathbf{A} = 1 + \frac{\mathbf{YZ}}{2} = 0{\cdot}7402 + j0{\cdot}150 \quad \textit{Ans.}$$

$$\therefore \mathbf{C} = 2 \times 2{\cdot}5 \,.\, 10^{-3}\angle 90^\circ\left(1 + 2{\cdot}5 \,.\, 10^{-3}\angle 90^\circ \,.\, \frac{120\angle 60^\circ}{2}\right)$$

$$= j5 \,.\, 10^{-3}(1 + 0{\cdot}15\angle 150^\circ)$$

$$= j5 \,.\, 10^{-3}[1 + 0{\cdot}075(-\sqrt{3} + j)]$$

$$= j5 \,.\, 10^{-3}(0{\cdot}8701 + j0{\cdot}075)$$

$$\therefore \mathbf{C} = (-0{\cdot}375 + j4{\cdot}3505) \,.\, 10^{-3} \text{ mho} \quad \textit{Ans.}$$

The characteristic impedance $\mathbf{Z_0} = \sqrt{\mathbf{Z_{OC}} \cdot \mathbf{Z_{SC}}}$

$$\therefore \mathbf{Z_0} = \sqrt{\frac{2\mathbf{Z_2}(\mathbf{Z} + 2\mathbf{Z_2})}{2\mathbf{Z_2} + \mathbf{Z} + 2\mathbf{Z_2}} \cdot \frac{2\mathbf{Z_2 Z}}{(2\mathbf{Z_2} + \mathbf{Z})}}$$

$$= \sqrt{\frac{\mathbf{Z} \,.\, 4\mathbf{Z_2}}{4 + \frac{\mathbf{Z}}{\mathbf{Z_2}}}} = \sqrt{\frac{\mathbf{Z}\frac{1}{\mathbf{Y}}}{1 + \frac{\mathbf{Z}}{4} \cdot \mathbf{Y}}}$$

$$= \sqrt{\frac{\dfrac{120\angle 60^\circ}{2\times 2{\cdot}5\,.\,10^{-3}\angle 90^\circ}}{1+\dfrac{120}{4}\angle 60^\circ\,.\,2\times 2{\cdot}5\,.\,10^{-3}\angle 90^\circ}}$$

$$= \sqrt{\frac{24\angle -30^\circ}{1+150\,.\,10^{-3}\angle 150^\circ}}$$

$$= \sqrt{\frac{24\angle -30^\circ}{(0{\cdot}8701+j0{\cdot}075)10^{-3}}}$$

$$= \sqrt{\frac{24\,.\,10^3\angle -30^\circ}{0{\cdot}873\angle 4^\circ{\cdot}54'}}$$

$$= 166\angle -17^\circ{\cdot}27'\ \Omega \quad \textit{Ans.}$$

2. The bridge shown in Fig. 2.2 is used to measure the value of the unknown inductance L. Derive the conditions required for balance when $R_2 = R_3$.

Balance is obtained at a frequency of 400 c/s with R_1, R, and R_4 respectively equal to 100, 25·6, and 50 Ω and the ratio R_2/R_3 equal to unity. Determine the unknown inductance.

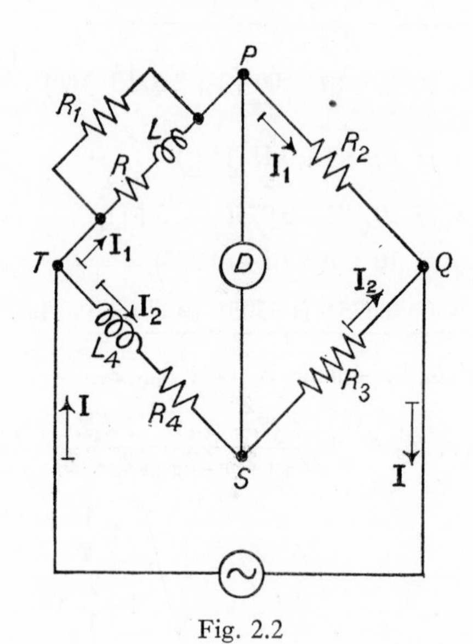

Fig. 2.2

Solution At balance evidently,

$$\mathbf{V}_{PT} = \mathbf{V}_{TS} \quad \text{and} \quad \mathbf{V}_{PQ} = \mathbf{V}_{QS}$$

$$\therefore \mathbf{I}_1\mathbf{Z}_{PT} = \mathbf{I}_2\mathbf{Z}_{TS}$$

and

$$\mathbf{I}_1\mathbf{Z}_{PQ} = \mathbf{I}_2\mathbf{Z}_{QS}$$

$$\therefore \mathbf{Z}_{PT}.\mathbf{Z}_{QS} = \mathbf{Z}_{PQ}.\mathbf{Z}_{TS} \text{ for balance}$$

$$\therefore \left[\frac{R_1(R+j\omega L)}{(R+R_1)+j\omega L}\right]R_3 = R_2(R_4+j\omega L_4)$$

$$\therefore R_1(R+j\omega L) = \frac{R_2}{R_3}(R_4+j\omega L_4)[(R+R_1)+j\omega L]$$

$$= \frac{R_2}{R_3}\left[R_4(R+R_1)-\omega^2 LL_4 + j\omega\{L_4(R+R_1)+LR_4\}\right]$$

$$\therefore R_1(R+j\omega L) = R_4(R+R_1)-\omega^2 LL_4+j\omega\{L_4(R+R_1)+LR_4\}$$

for either $R_2 = R_3$ or $R_2/R_3 = 1{\cdot}0$

$\therefore$ equating in phase components,

$$RR_1 = R_4(R+R_1)-\omega^2 LL_4 \tag{1}$$

$$\therefore R(R_1-R_4) = R_1R_4-\omega^2 LL_4 \tag{2}$$

$\therefore$ equating in quadrature components,

$$R_1L = L_4(R+R_1)+LR_4 \tag{3}$$

$$\therefore L(R_1-R_4) = L_4(R+R_1) \tag{4}$$

Substituting for L, obtained from equation (4), in equation (2),

$$\therefore R(R_1-R_4) = R_1R_4-\omega^2 L_4.\frac{L_4(R+R_1)}{R_1-R_4}$$

$$\therefore R(R_1-R_4)^2 = R_1R_4(R_1-R_4)-\omega^2 L_4^2(R+R_1)$$

$$\therefore R[(R_1-R_4)^2+\omega^2 L_4^2] = R_1R_4(R_1-R_4)-\omega^2 L_4^2 R_1$$

$$\therefore R = \frac{R_1R_4(R_1-R_4)-\omega^2 L_4^2 R_1}{(R_1-R_4)^2+\omega^2 L_4^2}\ \Omega \tag{5}$$

From equations (4) and (5),

$$\therefore\ L(R_1-R_4) = L_4\left[\frac{R_1R_4(R_1-R_4)-\omega^2L_4{}^2R_1}{(R_1-R_4)^2+\omega^2L_4{}^2}+R_1\right]$$

$$= L_4\left[\frac{R_1R_4(R_1-R_4)-\omega^2L_4{}^2R_1 + R_1(R_1-R_4)^2+R_1\omega^2L_4{}^2}{(R_1-R_4)^2+\omega^2L_4{}^2}\right]$$

$$\therefore\ L = \frac{L_4R_1{}^2}{(R_1-R_4)^2+\omega^2L_4{}^2}\ \text{H} \qquad (6)$$

Equations (5) and (6) being the condition for balance

Given $R_1 = 100\ \Omega$; $R = 25{\cdot}6\ \Omega$; $R_4 = 50\ \Omega$; $f = 400$ c/s

Note: Since L_4 is not given it would be possible to rearrange equations (5) and (6) in order to eliminate L_4. This involves further algebraic manipulation which is unnecessary. Find L_4 from equation (5) and substitute in equation (6).

From equation (5)

$$R = 25{\cdot}6 = \frac{5.10^3\times50-\omega^2L_4{}^2.10^2}{(50)^2+\omega^2L_4{}^2}$$

$$\therefore\ 25{\cdot}6(25.10^2+\omega^2L_4{}^2) = 25.10^4-\omega^2L_4{}^2.10^2$$

$$\therefore\ \omega^2L_4{}^2(125{\cdot}6) = 25.10^4-25{\cdot}6\times25\times10^2$$

$$\therefore\ \omega^2L_4{}^2 = \frac{18{\cdot}6\times10^4}{125{\cdot}6} = 0{\cdot}148\times10^4$$

$$\therefore\ \omega L_4 = 0{\cdot}385\times10^2\ \Omega$$

$$\therefore\ L_4 = \frac{0{\cdot}385\times10^2}{2\pi\times400} = 1{\cdot}53.10^{-2}\ \text{H}$$

$\therefore$ from equation (6)

$$L = \frac{1{\cdot}53.10^{-2}\times10^4}{25.10^2+0{\cdot}148\times10^4} = \frac{1{\cdot}53}{39{\cdot}8}$$

$$= 38{\cdot}4\ \text{mH}\quad \textit{Ans.}$$

3. A direct voltage from a source of zero impedance is suddenly applied across the terminals of the circuit shown below. Derive an expression for the subsequent variation with time of the voltage across L_1.

If $C = 0{\cdot}02\,\mu F$, $L = 50$ mH, and $L_1 = 10$ mH, and the applied voltage is 11 kV, calculate the maximum value of the voltage across L_1. Determine also the time in which this value is first attained.

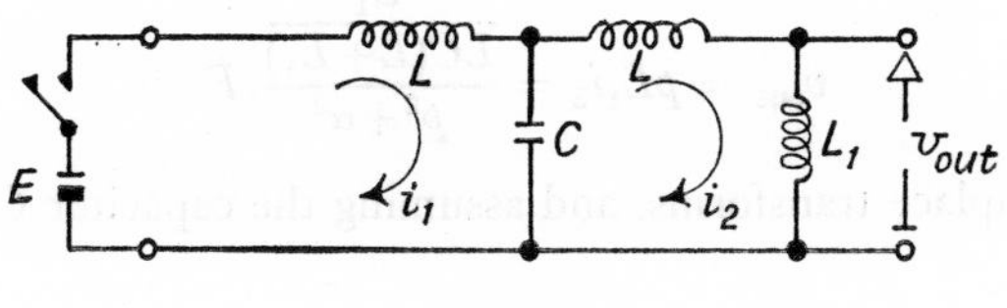

Fig. 2.3

The conventional directions of current, and voltage were not shown in the original equation.

Solution Using the principle of Maxwell's circulating currents to the two closed meshes,

$$pLi_1+\frac{1}{pC}(i_1-i_2) = E$$

and $$pLi_2+pL_1i_2+\frac{1}{pC}(i_2-i_1) = 0$$

where pL and $1/pC$ are operational reactances and $p = j\omega$.

$$\therefore\ i_1\left(pL+\frac{1}{pC}\right)-i_2\frac{1}{pC} = E$$

and $$-i_1\frac{1}{pC}+i_2\left(pL+pL_1+\frac{1}{pC}\right) = 0$$

$$\therefore\ i_1\left(pL+\frac{1}{pC}\right)\frac{1}{pC}-i_2\frac{1}{pC}\cdot\frac{1}{pC} = \frac{1}{pC}\cdot E \qquad (1)$$

and $$-i_1\left(pL+\frac{1}{pC}\right)\frac{1}{pC}+i_2\left(pL+\frac{1}{pC}\right)\left[p(L+L_1)+\frac{1}{pC}\right] = 0 \qquad (2)$$

Adding equations (1) and (2).

$$i_2\left[-\frac{1}{pC}\cdot\frac{1}{pC}+\left(pL+\frac{1}{pC}\right)\left\{p(L+L_1)+\frac{1}{pC}\right\}\right] = E\cdot\frac{1}{pC}$$

$$\therefore\ i_2 = \frac{E}{p^3LC(L+L_1)+\frac{1}{pC}-\frac{1}{pC}+pL+p(L+L_1)}$$

$$= \frac{E}{p[p^2LC(L+L_1)+(2L+L_1)]}$$

$$= \frac{\frac{1}{LC(L+L_1)}}{p(p^2+\alpha^2)}.E \quad \text{where} \quad \alpha^2 = \frac{2L+L_1}{LC(L+L_1)}$$

Now
$$v_{out} = pL_1i_2 = \frac{\frac{L_1}{LC(L+L_1)}}{p^2+\alpha^2}.E$$

Taking Laplace transforms, and assuming the capacitor C is initially uncharged:

$$\bar{v}_{out} = \frac{L_1}{LC(L+L_1)}\cdot\frac{1}{p_2+\alpha^2}\cdot\frac{E}{p} \quad \text{for a step input}$$

$$= \frac{L_1}{LC}\cdot\frac{E}{L+L_1}\cdot\frac{1}{\alpha^2}\cdot\frac{\alpha^2}{p(p^2+\alpha^2)}$$

$$= \frac{L_1}{LC}\cdot\frac{E}{L+L_1}\cdot\frac{LC(L+L_1)}{2L+L_1}\cdot\frac{\alpha^2}{p(p^2+\alpha^2)}$$

∴ from tables of inverse Laplace transforms,

$$v_{out} = \frac{EL_1}{2L+L_1}\cdot(1-\cos\alpha t) \quad \textit{Ans.}$$

The maximum value of v_{out} occurs when $\cos\alpha t = -1$ or $\alpha t = \pi$ in the first case.

$$\therefore \text{ maximum value of } v_{out} = \frac{2EL_1}{2L+L_1}$$

Given $L = 50$ mH, $L_1 = 10$ mH, $E = 11$ kV, $C = 0{\cdot}02$ μF

$$\therefore v_{out}\,(\text{maximum}) = \frac{2\times 11\times 10}{100+10} = 2 \text{ kV} \quad \textit{Ans.}$$

The time at which this first occurs is given by

$$t = \frac{\pi}{\alpha} = \frac{\pi}{\sqrt{\frac{2L+L_1}{LC(L+L_1)}}} = \frac{\pi}{\sqrt{\frac{110.10^{-3}}{50.10^{-3}\times 0{\cdot}02.10^{-6}\times 60.10^{-3}}}}$$

$$= \frac{\pi}{10^4\sqrt{110/6}}$$

$$= 73{\cdot}5 \text{ μs} \quad \textit{Ans.}$$

4. Show, from a consideration of the general expression for the distribution of voltage and current along a transmission line, that the input reactance of a short-circuited loss-free line of length l is given by:

$$X = \sqrt{L/C} \tan \omega l \sqrt{LC}$$

where L and C represent the inductance and capacitance per unit length of line and ω is the angular frequency.

Sketch the variation in X when the length of line is varied from zero to one wavelength. What will be the effect of a small amount of loss in the line?

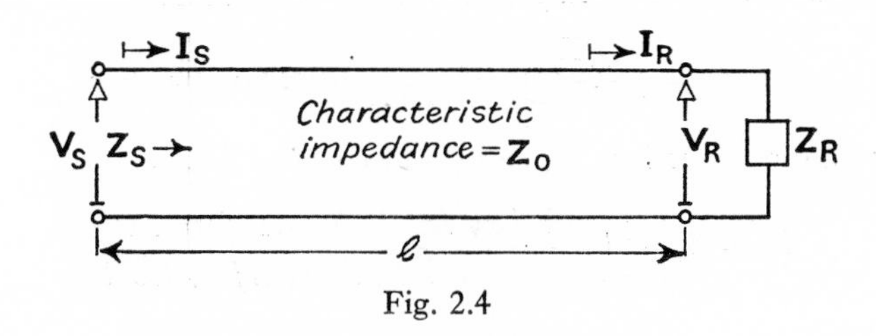

Fig. 2.4

Solution The general line equations are:

$$\mathbf{V_S} = \mathbf{V_R} \cosh \gamma l + \mathbf{I_R Z_0} \sinh \gamma l \tag{1}$$

$$\mathbf{I_S} = \frac{\mathbf{V_R}}{\mathbf{Z_0}} \sinh \gamma l + \mathbf{I_R} \cosh \gamma l \tag{2}$$

$\therefore$ The input impedance

$$\mathbf{Z_S} = \frac{\mathbf{V_S}}{\mathbf{I_S}} = \frac{\mathbf{I_R Z_R} \cosh \gamma l + \mathbf{I_R Z_0} \sinh \gamma l}{\mathbf{I_R} \cosh \gamma l + \frac{\mathbf{I_R Z_R}}{\mathbf{Z_0}} . \sinh \gamma l} \quad \text{since } \mathbf{V_R} = \mathbf{I_R Z_R}$$

$$\therefore \mathbf{Z_S} = \mathbf{Z_0} \left[\frac{\mathbf{Z_R} \cosh \gamma l + \mathbf{Z_0} \sinh \gamma l}{\mathbf{Z_0} \cosh \gamma l + \mathbf{Z_R} \sinh \gamma l} \right] \tag{3}$$

The propagation constant $\gamma = \alpha + j\beta$, where α = the attenuation in nepers = 0 for a lossless line and β = the phase change in radians/unit length. Now the distance along the line such that the phase change is 2π rad is called the wavelength λ

$$\therefore \lambda\beta = 2\pi \quad \text{or} \quad \underline{\beta = \frac{2\pi}{\lambda}} \tag{4}$$

Also $$\gamma = \sqrt{(R + jwL)(G + jwC)}$$

where R = resistance per unit length of the uniform transmission line = 0 for a lossless line.

ωL = inductive reactance, per unit length.

G = the conductance per unit length in mho = 0 for a lossless line.

ωC = capacitive susceptance, per unit length.

$\therefore\ \gamma = \alpha + j\beta = 0 + j\omega\sqrt{LC}$ for a lossless line

$$\therefore\ \beta = \omega\sqrt{LC} \tag{5}$$

Also the characteristic impedance of the uniform line

$$= \mathbf{Z}_0 = \sqrt{\frac{R+j\omega L}{G+j\omega C}} = \sqrt{\frac{L}{C}} \quad \text{for a loss-free line} \tag{6}$$

Substituting equations (5) and (6) in equation (3),

$$\mathbf{Z_S} = \mathbf{Z}_0\left[\frac{\mathbf{Z_R}\cosh j\omega\sqrt{LC}.l + \mathbf{Z}_0 \sinh j\omega\sqrt{LC}.l}{\mathbf{Z}_0\cosh j\omega\sqrt{LC}.l + \mathbf{Z_R}\sinh j\omega\sqrt{LC}.l}\right]$$

$$= \mathbf{Z}_0\left[\frac{\mathbf{Z_R}\cos\omega\sqrt{LC}.l + j\mathbf{Z}_0\sin\omega\sqrt{LC}.l}{\mathbf{Z}_0\cos\omega\sqrt{LC}.l + j\mathbf{Z_R}\sin\omega\sqrt{LC}.l}\right]$$

$\therefore$ When the termination is a short circuit, i.e. $\mathbf{Z_R} = 0$, then

$$\mathbf{Z_S} = j\sqrt{L/C}\tan\omega\sqrt{LC}.l = 0 + jX$$

$$\therefore\ X = \sqrt{L/C}\tan\omega l\sqrt{LC}. \quad \text{Q.E.D.}$$

$$= \sqrt{\frac{L}{C}}\tan\frac{2\pi}{\lambda}\cdot l\,\Omega$$

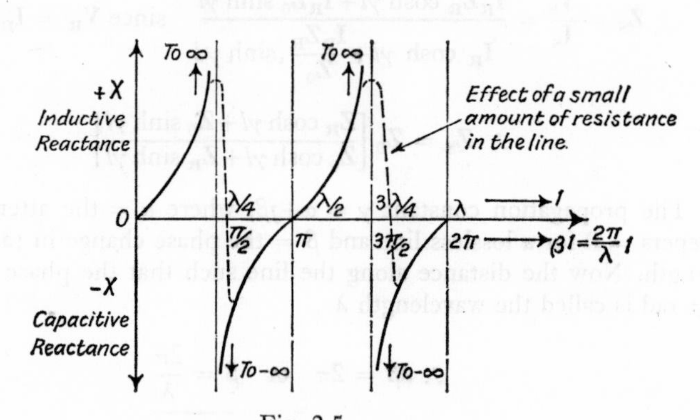

Fig. 2.5
The variation in X as l varies from 0 to λ

From equation (3),

$$\mathbf{Z_S} = \mathbf{Z_0} \tanh \gamma l \quad \text{when} \quad \mathbf{Z_R} = 0$$

hence the inclusion of a small amount of resistance will mean that the input impedance is complex, and not purely inductively or capacitively reactive. Also at $l = \lambda/4, 3\lambda/4$, the input impedance will not be infinite, but a finite value, and tend to follow the dotted lines on the rough sketch of the variation of X. There will also be a small amount of attenuation along the line.

5. A 3-phase, 4-wire system supplies loads which are unequally distributed on the three phases. An analysis of the current flowing in the direction of the loads in the R, Y, and B lines shows that in the R line the positive phase sequence component of current is $200\angle 0°$ A, and the negative phase sequence current is $100\angle 60°$ A. The total observed current flowing back to the supply in the neutral conductor is $300\angle 300°$ A. Calculate the currents in phase and magnitude in the three lines.

Assuming that the 3-phase supply voltages are symmetrical and that the power factor of the load on the R phase is $\frac{1}{2}\sqrt{3}$ leading, determine the power factor of the loads on the two other phases.

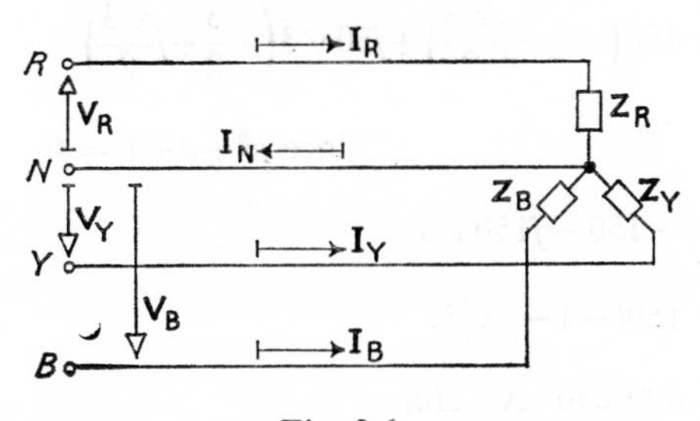

Fig. 2.6

Solution 1. Using the conventional directions of voltage and current as illustrated in the circuit diagram shown above.

2. Assume a phase sequence of RYB.
3. Using the positive phase sequence component in the R line as the reference vector.

Now the positive phase sequence component of current in the R line:

$$= \mathbf{I}_1 = 200\angle 0° = 200(1+j0) \text{ A}, \quad \text{the reference vector}$$

The negative phase sequence component of current in the R line:

$$= \mathbf{I}_2 = 100\underline{/60^\circ} = 50(1+j\sqrt{3})\ \text{A}$$

The zero phase sequence component of current

$$= \mathbf{I}_0 = \tfrac{1}{3}[\mathbf{I}_R+\mathbf{I}_Y+\mathbf{I}_B] = \tfrac{1}{3}.\mathbf{I}_N$$

$$= \tfrac{1}{3}.300\underline{/300^\circ}$$

$$= 50(1-j\sqrt{3})\ \text{A}$$

Now $\mathbf{I}_R = \mathbf{I}_1+\mathbf{I}_2+\mathbf{I}_0$

$$= 200+50+j50\sqrt{3}+50-j50\sqrt{3}$$

$$= \underline{300\underline{/0^\circ}\ \text{A}}\quad \textit{Ans.}$$

and $\mathbf{I}_Y = a^2\mathbf{I}_1+a\mathbf{I}_2+\mathbf{I}_0$

$$= 200a^2+50a(1+j\sqrt{3})+50(1-j\sqrt{3})$$

$$= 150a^2+(50a^2+50a+50)+j50\sqrt{3}(a-1$$

$$= 150\left(-\tfrac{1}{2}-j\frac{\sqrt{3}}{2}\right)+j50\sqrt{3}\left(-\frac{3}{2}+j\frac{\sqrt{3}}{2}\right)$$

since $a^2+a+1 = 0$

$$= -150-j150\sqrt{3}$$

$$= 150(-1-j\sqrt{3})$$

$$= \underline{300\underline{/240^\circ}\ \text{A}}\quad \textit{Ans.}$$

and $\mathbf{I}_B = a\mathbf{I}_1+a^2\mathbf{I}_2+\mathbf{I}_0$

$$= 200a+50a^2(1+j\sqrt{3})+50(1-j\sqrt{3})$$

$$= (50a^2+50a+50)+150a+j50\sqrt{3}(a^2-1$$

$$= 150\left(-\tfrac{1}{2}+j\frac{\sqrt{3}}{2}\right)+j50\sqrt{3}\left(-\frac{3}{2}-j\frac{\sqrt{3}}{2}\right)$$

$$= \underline{0}\quad \textit{Ans.}$$

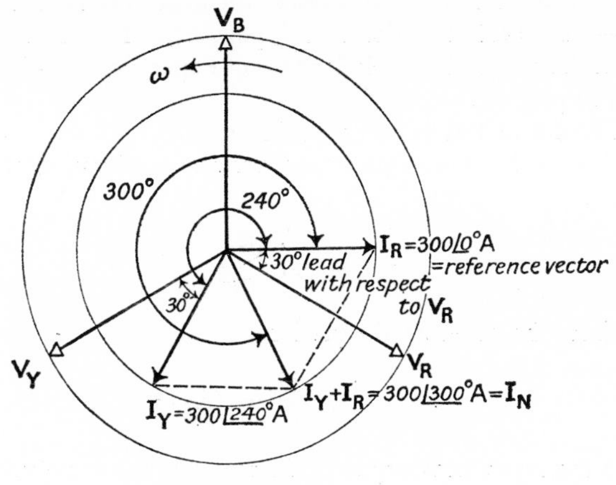

Fig. 2.7

From the vector diagram $\mathbf{I_Y}$ leads $\mathbf{V_Y}$ by 30°.

$$\therefore \text{ power factor in the yellow phase } = \cos 30° = \frac{\sqrt{3}}{2} \text{ lead.}$$

Since $\mathbf{I_B} = 0$, there is no power factor in the B phase. *Ans.*

Note: The vector diagram checks that

$$\mathbf{I_R}+\mathbf{I_Y} = \mathbf{I_N} = 300\underline{/300°} \text{ A}$$

6. Describe briefly the essentials of a simple remote-position-control servo-mechanism stabilized by direct velocity feedback, and show that its operation is characterized by differential equation of the form:

$$\frac{1}{\omega_n{}^2}\cdot\frac{d^2\theta_o}{dt^2}+T\frac{d\theta_o}{dt}+\theta_o = \theta_i$$

The position of a rotatable mass driven by an electric motor is controlled from a handwheel. The damping torques due to viscous friction and velocity feedback, respectively are equal. The moment of inertia of the moving parts referred to the mass is 100 kg-m², and the undamped natural frequency is 2·5 c/s. If the motion is critically damped, calculate the feedback torque per unit angular velocity and the steady-state angular misalignment when the input angle is varied at the rate of 1 rad/s.

Solution For the derivation of the differential equation see Paper No. IV—June 1961, question No. 7, page 61. The essentials of the system are indicated in the block diagram of Paper No. VI—June 1962, question No. 2, page 80.

Given $J = 100$ kg-m², $f_n = 215$ c/s

Now in the steady-state condition the acceleration of the output shaft ceases

$$\therefore \frac{d^2\theta_o}{dt^2} = 0$$

∴ from the differential equation

$$T.\frac{d\theta_o}{dt} = (\theta_i - \theta_o)$$

Also the input and output shafts rotate at the same velocity

$$\therefore \frac{d\theta_o}{dt} = \frac{d\theta_i}{dt} = \frac{1}{T}(\theta_i - \theta_o)$$

Now for critical damping $\omega_n T = 2$

$$\therefore T = \frac{2}{\omega_n} = \frac{2}{2\pi \times 2{\cdot}5} \text{ s}$$

and

$$\frac{d\theta_i}{dt} = 1 \text{ rad/s}$$

$$\therefore (\theta_i - \theta_o) = T\frac{d\theta_i}{dt} = \frac{2}{5\pi} \times 1 \text{ rad}$$

$$= \left(\frac{2}{5\pi} \times \frac{180}{\pi}\right)^\circ$$

$= 7{\cdot}3^\circ$ (the steady-state angular misalignment sometimes called the velocity lag) *Ans.*

Now $T = F/J\omega_n^2$, derived in the proof of the differential equation.

$$\therefore F = TJ\omega_n^2 = \frac{2}{\omega_n} \times 100 \times \omega_n^2 = 2 \times 100 \times 2\pi \times 2{\cdot}5 \text{ Nm/rad/sec}$$

$= 1000\pi$ = the total damping torque due to viscous friction and velocity feedback

∴ The feedback torque per unit angular velocity

$= 500\pi = 1571{\cdot}5$ Nm/rad/s *Ans.*

PAPER NO. III—NOVEMBER 1960

1. Derive an expression for the time variation of the current obtained when a short-circuit is suddenly applied to a sinusoidal a.c. source with an inductive-resistive internal impedance.

Hence calculate approximately the largest possible peak current obtained when a 50 c/s source is short-circuited. The e.m.f. is 200 V r.m.s. and the internal impedance is represented by an inductance of 15 mH in series with a resistance of 0·08 Ω.

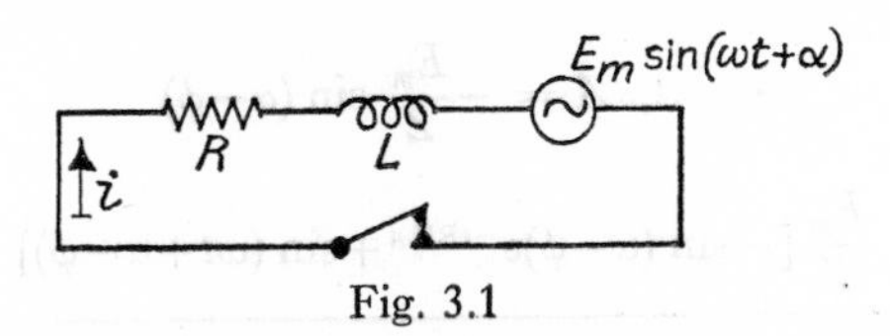

Fig. 3.1

Solution Applying Kirchhoff's second law to the circuit:

$$L\frac{di}{dt}+Ri = E_m \sin(\omega t+\alpha)$$

$$\therefore\ i\left(D+\frac{R}{L}\right) = \frac{E_m}{L}.\sin(\omega t+\alpha)$$

where D = d/dt.

The transient solution is given by the complementary function, i.e.:

$$i\left(D+\frac{R}{L}\right) = 0$$

$$\therefore\ i = A\varepsilon^{-Rt/L}$$

where A is a constant.

The steady-state solution is given by the particular integral, i.e.:

$$\frac{1}{D+R/L}\cdot\frac{E_m}{L}\cdot\sin(\omega t+\alpha) = \frac{D-R/L}{D^2-(R/L)^2}\cdot\frac{E_m}{L}\cdot\sin(\omega t+\alpha)$$

$$= \frac{D-(R/L)}{-\omega^2-(R/L)^2}\cdot\frac{E_m}{L}\cdot\sin(\omega t+\alpha)$$

$$= \frac{R-DL}{R^2+(\omega L)^2}\cdot E_m\cdot\sin(\omega t+\alpha)$$

$$= \frac{E_m}{Z}\left[\frac{R}{Z}\cdot\sin(\omega t+\alpha)-\frac{\omega L}{Z}\cos(\omega t+\alpha)\right]$$

$$= \frac{E_m}{Z}\cdot\sin(\omega t+\alpha-\phi)$$

where $\phi = \tan^{-1}(\omega L/R)$ and $Z = \sqrt{R^2+(\omega L)^2}$.

∴ the complete solution is:

$$i = A\varepsilon^{-(R/L)t}+\frac{E_m}{Z}\cdot\sin(\omega t+\alpha-\phi)$$

When $t = 0$, $i = 0$

$$\therefore\ A = -\frac{E_m}{Z}\cdot\sin(\alpha-\phi)$$

$$\therefore\ i = \frac{E_m}{Z}[-\sin(\alpha-\phi)\varepsilon^{-(R/L)t}+\sin(\omega t+\alpha-\phi)]\ \text{A} \quad \textit{Ans.}$$

Assuming the exponent decay term $\varepsilon^{-(R/L)t} \to 1{\cdot}0$, i.e. the decay is small, the maximum value of the transient term occurs when $\alpha-\phi = 3\pi/2$. Therefore, $-\sin(\alpha-\phi) = +1$. The maximum value of the steady-state term, $\sin(\omega t+\alpha-\phi)$, is also unity.

∴ approximate maximum value of i is $2E_m/Z$.

Now $\quad Z = \sqrt{(0{\cdot}08)^2+(2\pi.50{\cdot}15.10^{-3})} \simeq 1{\cdot}5\pi$

$$\therefore\ I_m = \frac{2\times 200\sqrt{2}}{1{\cdot}5\pi} = 120\ \text{A} \quad \textit{Ans.}$$

Note: Laplace transforms are not used in this problem as the circuit is simple, and the standard method using the operator D is well known. In this particular problem the method using Laplace transforms is longer, and requires considerable mathematical manipulation to obtain the solution in the standard form.

2. A cable 8 miles long has the following constants per loop-mile: resistance, 45 Ω; inductance, 0·35 mH; capacitance, 0·13 μF. The shunt conductance may be neglected.

Calculate the characteristic impedance of the cable at 5,000 c/s. If the load impedance at the receiving end has this value and a voltage of 200 V at 5,000 c/s is applied at the sending end, calculate (*a*) the magnitude of the receiving end current, (*b*) the wavelength, and (*c*) the velocity of propagation.

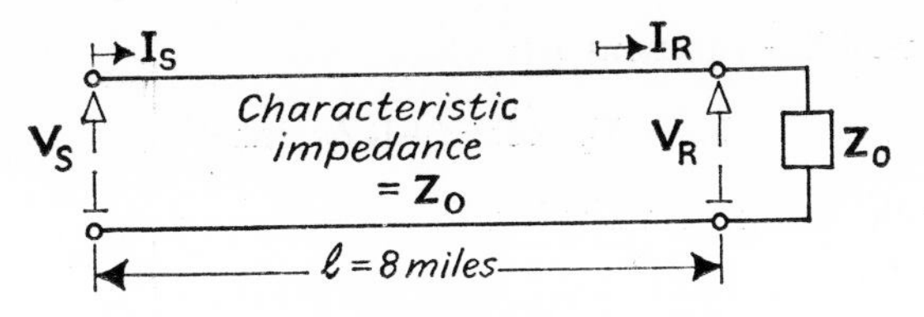

Fig. 3.2

Solution Given $R = 45\ \Omega$ per loop-mile, $L = 0{\cdot}35$ mH per loop-mile, $C = 0{\cdot}13\ \mu$F per loop-mile, $G = 0$, $f = 5{,}000$ c/s.

Now $\omega L = 2\pi \times 5{\cdot}10^3 - 0{\cdot}35.10^{-3}\ \Omega = 11\ \Omega$

$$\omega C = 2\pi \times 5.10^3 \times 0{\cdot}13.10^{-6} \text{ mho} = 40{\cdot}8.10^{-4} \text{ mho}$$

$$Z_0 = \sqrt{\frac{R+j\omega L}{G+j\omega C}} = \sqrt{\frac{45+j11}{j40{\cdot}8.10^{-4}}} = \frac{10^2}{6{\cdot}38}\sqrt{11-j45}$$

$$= 15{\cdot}7\sqrt{46{\cdot}3\underline{/-76^\circ.16'}} = 106{\cdot}9(\cos 38^\circ.8' - j \sin 39^\circ.8')$$

$$= \underline{(84-j66)\ \Omega} = \text{the characteristic impendance} \quad \textit{Ans.}$$

Now the propagation constant $\gamma = \sqrt{(R+j\omega L)(G+j\omega C)}$.

$$\therefore \gamma = \sqrt{(45+j11)(j40{\cdot}8.10^{-4})}$$

$$= 6{\cdot}39.10^{-2}\sqrt{-11+j45}$$

$$= 6{\cdot}39 \times 6{\cdot}8.10^{-2} \underline{\Big/ \frac{103^\circ.44'}{2}}$$

$$= 43{\cdot}5(\cos 51^\circ.52' + j \sin 51^\circ.52').10^{-2}$$

$$= 0{\cdot}268 + j0{\cdot}342 = \alpha + j\beta$$

Now the wavelength $\lambda = \dfrac{2\pi}{\beta} = \dfrac{2\pi}{0{\cdot}342}$

$$= \underline{18{\cdot}4 \text{ miles}} \quad \textit{Ans. (b)}$$

Velocity of propagation $= f\lambda = \dfrac{f2\pi}{\beta} = \dfrac{\omega}{\beta}$

$$= \frac{2\pi \times 5.10^3}{0{\cdot}342}$$

$$= \underline{92{,}000 \text{ mile/s}} \quad \textit{Ans. (c)}$$

The general line equations are:

$$\mathbf{V_S} = \mathbf{V_R} \cosh \gamma l + \mathbf{I_R Z_0} \sinh \gamma l$$

and when the line is terminated in $\mathbf{Z_0}$,

$$\mathbf{V_R} = \mathbf{I_R Z_0}$$

$$\therefore \mathbf{V_S} = \mathbf{I_R Z_0}\left(\frac{\varepsilon^{\gamma l}+\varepsilon^{-\gamma l}}{2}+\frac{\varepsilon^{\gamma l}-\varepsilon^{-\gamma l}}{2}\right)$$

$$= \mathbf{I_R Z_0}\varepsilon^{\gamma l}$$

$$\therefore \mathbf{I_R} = \frac{\mathbf{V_S}}{\mathbf{Z_0}}\varepsilon^{-\gamma l}$$

$$= \frac{200}{84-j66}\varepsilon^{-(0\cdot268j0\cdot342)8}$$

$$= \frac{84-j66}{200}\varepsilon^{-2\cdot14}\varepsilon^{-j2\cdot74}$$

$$\therefore |\mathbf{I_R}| = I_R = \frac{200}{\sqrt{84^2+66^2}}\cdot\varepsilon^{-2\cdot14}\times 1$$

$$= \frac{106\cdot9}{200}\times\frac{8\cdot499}{1}$$

$$= \underline{220 \text{ mA}} \quad \textit{Ans. (a)}$$

3. Define the term 'form factor' and give an example of its use in electrical measurements.

Derive a general expression for the form factor of a complex wave containing odd-order harmonics. Hence, calculate the form factor of the alternating current represented by,

$$i = 2\cdot5 \sin 157t + 0\cdot7 \sin 471t + 0\cdot4 \sin 785t$$

Solution Form factor $= \dfrac{\text{the r.m.s. value of a waveform taken over a period}}{\text{the average value of the same waveform taken over the same period}}$

With sine waves the period taken is normally half a complete period, i.e.: $0-\pi$.

Example of the use of the form factor in electrical measurements

When using a moving-coil meter, which indicates d.c., in conjunction with a full wave bridge rectifier, to measure a.c. the resulting rectified current will be as shown in Fig. 3.3 The moving-coil instrument will

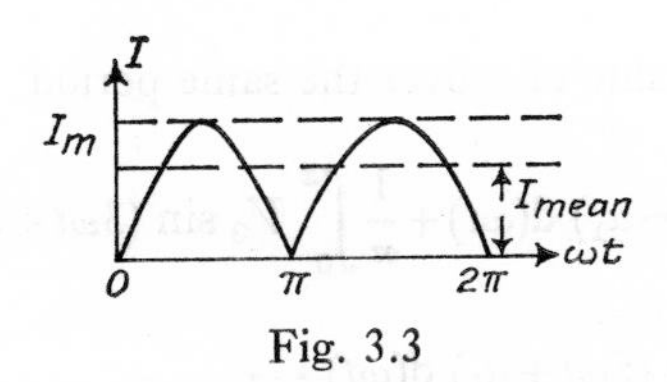

Fig. 3.3

indicate a reading proportional to I_{mean}, but is required to indicate $I_{\text{r.m.s.}}$

Now $$I_{\text{mean}} = 0{\cdot}637 I_{\text{max}} = 0{\cdot}9 I_{\text{r.m.s.}}$$

$$\therefore \quad \frac{I_{\text{r.m.s.}}}{I_{\text{mean}}} = 1{\cdot}11 \text{ for a sine wave}$$

Hence, the reading of the d.c. moving-coil meter would have to be multiplied by 1·11 to give the r.m.s. value of the current, the figure 1·11 being the form factor.

Let a complex wave containing only odd-order harmonics

$$= v = V_1 \sin(\omega t+\alpha_1)+V_3 \sin(3\omega t+\alpha_3)+V_5 \sin(5\omega t+\alpha_5)+\cdots$$

Now $$(v_{\text{r.m.s.}})^2 = \frac{1}{\pi}\int_0^\pi v^2 \,\mathrm{d}(\omega t)$$

$$= \frac{1}{\pi}\int_0^\pi V_1^2 \sin^2(\omega t+\alpha_1)\,\mathrm{d}(\omega t)$$

$$+\frac{1}{\pi}\int_0^\pi V_3^2 \sin^2(3\omega t+\alpha_3)\,\mathrm{d}(\omega t)$$

$$+\frac{1}{\pi}\int_0^\pi V_5^2 \sin^2(5\omega t+\alpha_5)\,\mathrm{d}(\omega t)+\cdots$$

$$+\frac{1}{\pi}\int_0^\pi V_1 V_3 \sin(\omega t+\alpha_1)\sin(3\omega t+\alpha_3)\,\mathrm{d}(\omega t)+\cdots$$

$$= \frac{V_1^2}{2\pi}\left[\omega t - \frac{\sin(2)(\omega t+\alpha_1)}{2}\right]_0^\pi$$

$$+\frac{V_3^2}{2\pi}\left[\omega t - \frac{\sin(2)(3\omega t+\alpha_3)}{2}\right]_0^\pi + \cdots$$

$$= \frac{V_1^2}{2}+\frac{V_3^2}{2}+\frac{V_5^2}{2}+\cdots$$

Note that $$\int_0^{\pi} (\text{products of sines})\, d(\omega t) = 0$$

$$\therefore \text{ r.m.s. value} = \frac{1}{\sqrt{2}} \sqrt{V_1^2 + V_3^2 + V_5^2 + \cdots}$$

Now the average value of v over the same period

$$= \frac{1}{\pi}\int_0^{\pi} V_1 \sin(\omega t + \alpha_1)\, d(\omega t) + \frac{1}{\pi}\int_0^{\pi} V_3 \sin(3\omega t + \alpha_3)\, d(\omega t)$$

$$+ \frac{1}{\pi}\int_0^{\pi} V_5 \sin(5\omega t + \alpha_5)\, d(\omega t) \cdots$$

$$= \frac{V_1}{\pi}\Big[-\cos(\omega t + \alpha_1)\Big]_0^{\pi} + \frac{V_3}{\pi}\left[-\frac{\cos(3\omega t + \alpha_3)}{3}\right]_0^{\pi}$$

$$+ \frac{V_5}{\pi}\left[-\frac{\cos 5(\omega t + a_5)}{5}\right]_0^{\pi}$$

$$= V_1 \frac{2}{\pi} \cdot \cos \alpha_1 + V_3 \frac{2}{3\pi} \cos \alpha_3 + V_5 \frac{2}{5\pi} \cos \alpha_5$$

$$= \frac{2}{\pi}\left[\frac{V_1 \cos \alpha_1}{1} + \frac{V_3 \cos \alpha_3}{3} + \frac{V_5 \cos \alpha_5}{5} + \cdots\right]$$

$$\therefore \text{ Form factor} = \frac{\pi}{2\sqrt{2}} \cdot \frac{\sqrt{V_1^2 + V_3^2 + V_5^2 + \cdots}}{\left(\frac{V_1 \cos \alpha_1}{1} + \frac{V_3 \cos \alpha_3}{3} + \frac{V_5 \cos \alpha_5}{5} + \cdots\right)}$$ *Ans.*

If the angles $\alpha_1 = \alpha_3 = \alpha_5 = 0$

$$\therefore \text{ Form factor} = \frac{\pi}{2\sqrt{2}} \cdot \frac{\sqrt{V_1^2 + V_3^2 + V_5^2 + \cdots}}{\left(\frac{V_1}{1} + \frac{V_3}{3} + \frac{V_5}{5} + \cdots\right)}$$

Using the figures given, the form factor for i

$$= \frac{\pi}{2\sqrt{2}} \frac{\sqrt{2{\cdot}5^2 + 0{\cdot}7^2 + 0{\cdot}4^2}}{\left(\frac{2{\cdot}5}{1} + \frac{0{\cdot}7}{3} + \frac{0{\cdot}4}{5}\right)} = \underline{0{\cdot}992}$$ *Ans.*

N.B. The expression given for i is almost a square wave of form factor 1·0.

4. A balanced 3-phase, 3-wire supply is connected to the terminals A, B, C as shown in Fig. 3.4. The line voltage is 400 V. A star-connected load comprising a resistor and two equal pure inductors is connected as shown in the figure, and a wattmeter W is connected in the position shown. If $R = 100\ \Omega$ and $X = 100\ \Omega$ determine the power indicated by the wattmeter for each of the sequences ABC and ACB.

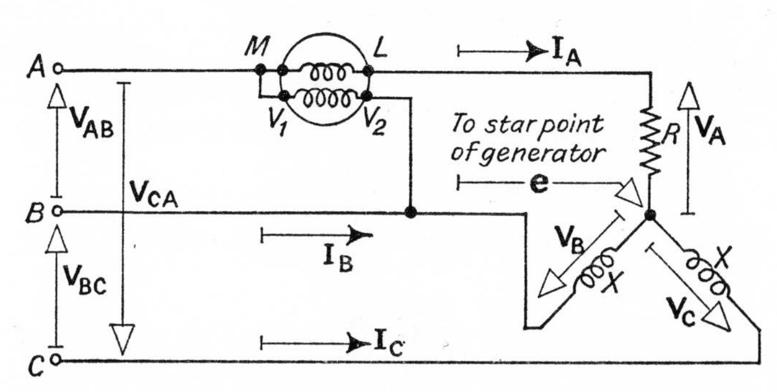

Fig. 3.4

Solution 1. Use the conventional directions of voltage and current as indicated in the figure (not shown in the original diagram).

2. Use the A-phase balanced generator voltage as a reference vector

$$\mathbf{E_A} = E(1+j0)$$

$$\therefore\ \mathbf{E_B} = a^2E$$

$$\therefore\ \mathbf{E_C} = aE$$

3. Assume that if current flows from M to L and $V_1 > V_2$ the wattmeter W reads positive (the current, and voltage coil designations M, L, V_1 and V_2 were not shown on the original circuit diagram).

4. Assume in the first instance that the phase sequence is ABC.

Now $$\mathbf{I_A} = \frac{\mathbf{V_A}}{100} = \frac{\mathbf{E_A}-\mathbf{e}}{100} = \frac{E-\mathbf{e}}{100}$$

and $$\mathbf{I_B} = \frac{\mathbf{V_B}}{j100} = \frac{\mathbf{E_B}-\mathbf{e}}{j100} = \frac{a^2E-\mathbf{e}}{j100}$$

and $$\mathbf{I_C} = \frac{\mathbf{V_C}}{j100} = \frac{\mathbf{E_C}-\mathbf{e}}{j100} = \frac{aE-\mathbf{e}}{j100}$$

Since the circuit is a 3-wire, 3-phase system, then

$$\mathbf{I_A}+\mathbf{I_B}+\mathbf{I_C}+0$$

$$\therefore \frac{E-\mathbf{e}}{100}+\frac{a^2E-\mathbf{e}}{j100}+\frac{aE-\mathbf{e}}{j100} = 0$$

$$\therefore \mathbf{e} = \frac{E(1-ja^2-ja)}{1-j2} = \frac{E(1+j)}{1-j2} = \frac{E}{5}(-1+j3)$$

Since
$$a^2 = -\tfrac{1}{2}-j\frac{\sqrt{3}}{2}$$

$$a = -\tfrac{1}{2}+j\frac{\sqrt{3}}{2}$$

$$\therefore \mathbf{I_A} = \frac{E-\frac{E}{5}(-1+j3)}{100} = \frac{E}{500}\cdot(6-j3)$$

$$= \frac{400}{\sqrt{3}}\cdot\frac{3}{500}(2-j)$$

$$= \frac{4\sqrt{3}}{5}\cdot(2-j)\text{ A}$$

Now $\mathbf{V_{AB}} = \mathbf{V_A}-\mathbf{V_B} = E(1-a^2) = \frac{400}{\sqrt{3}}\cdot\frac{1}{2}(3+j\sqrt{3})\text{ V}$

The wattmeter W reads the dot product of:

$$\mathbf{V_{AB}}.\mathbf{I_A} = \frac{200}{\sqrt{3}}\cdot\frac{4\sqrt{3}}{5}\cdot(3+j\sqrt{3})(2-j)$$

$$= 160(6-\sqrt{3}) = 683\text{ W with sequence } ABC \quad \textit{Ans.}$$

With the phase sequence ACB,

$$\frac{E-\mathbf{e}}{100}+\frac{aE-\mathbf{e}}{j100}+\frac{a^2E-\mathbf{e}}{j100} = 0$$

$$\therefore \mathbf{e} = \frac{E}{5}(-1+j\sqrt{3})$$

and
$$\mathbf{I_A} = \frac{4\sqrt{3}}{5}(2-j)\text{ A}$$

Now $\mathbf{V_{AB}} = \mathbf{V_A}-\mathbf{V_B} = E(1-a) = \frac{400}{\sqrt{3}}\cdot\frac{1}{2}(3-j\sqrt{3})\text{ V}$

∴ The wattmeter W reads the dot product of:

$$\mathbf{V_{AB}} \cdot \mathbf{I_A} = \frac{200}{\sqrt{3}} \cdot \frac{4\sqrt{3}}{5}(3-j\sqrt{3})(2-j)$$

$$= 160(6+\sqrt{3})$$

$$= \underline{1238 \text{ W with the sequence } ACB} \quad \textit{Ans.}$$

Note: The dot product of two complex quantities $(a+jb)(c+jd) = (ac+bd)$, which is the power in a circuit. It is the vector product of two complex quantities, which produce a scalar quantity.

5. Derive expressions for the symmetrical components corresponding to an unbalanced system of 3-phase voltages V_a, V_b, V_c, where V_a, V_b, and V_c are given in complex notation and h is the sequence operator.

In a 3-phase 4-wire system the currents in the R, Y, and B lines under abnormal conditions of loading were as follows:

$$I_r = 100\underline{/30^\circ} \text{ A}, \quad I_y = 50\underline{/300^\circ} \text{ A}, \quad I_b = 30\underline{/180^\circ} \text{ A}$$

Calculate the positive, negative, and zero phase sequence currents in the R line, and the return current in the neutral conductor.

Solution An unsymmetrical set of 3-phase voltages or currents may be resolved into a number of symmetrical sets. The currents or voltages produced by each of the symmetrical sets may be added, using the principle of superposition, to give the resultant currents or voltages of the unsymmetrical set.

The symmetrical components of a set of 3-phase voltages are:

1. Positive sequence components which form a balanced set of 3-phase voltages of phase sequence ABC, designated

$$\mathbf{V}_1, \quad h^2\mathbf{V}_1, \quad h\mathbf{V}_1$$

2. Negative sequence components which form a balanced set of 3-phase voltages of phase sequence ACB, designated

$$\mathbf{V}_2, \quad h\mathbf{V}_2, \quad h^2\mathbf{V}_2$$

3. The zero sequence components which are equal in magnitude and in phase, designated

$$\mathbf{V}_0, \quad \mathbf{V}_0, \quad \mathbf{V}_0$$

$$\therefore \mathbf{V_a} = \mathbf{V}_1+\mathbf{V}_2+\mathbf{V}_0 \qquad (1)$$

$$\mathbf{V_b} = h^2\mathbf{V}_1+h\mathbf{V}_2+\mathbf{V}_0 \qquad (2)$$

$$\mathbf{V_c} = h\mathbf{V}_1+h^2\mathbf{V}_2+\mathbf{V}_0 \qquad (3)$$

Adding equations (1), (2), and (3)

$$\mathbf{V}_0 = \tfrac{1}{3}(\mathbf{V}_a+\mathbf{V}_b+\mathbf{V}_c) \qquad (4)$$

since $1+h+h^2 = 0$.

Adding $(1)+h(2)+h^2(3)$,

$$\mathbf{V}_1 = \tfrac{1}{3}(\mathbf{V}_a+h\mathbf{V}_b+h^2\mathbf{V}_c) \qquad (5)$$

since $h^3 = 1$ and $h^4 = h.h^3 = h$.

Adding $(1)+h^2(2)+h(3)$,

$$\mathbf{V}_2 = \tfrac{1}{3}(\mathbf{V}_a+h^2\mathbf{V}_b+h\mathbf{V}_c) \qquad (6)$$

Equations (4), (5), and (6) being the equations for the symmetrical components corresponding to an unbalanced system of 3-phase voltages $\mathbf{V}_a, \mathbf{V}_b, \mathbf{V}_c$.

Numerical portion

Given $\mathbf{I}_r = 100\underline{/30^\circ} = 100\left(\frac{\sqrt{3}}{2}+j\frac{1}{2}\right) = 50(\sqrt{3}+j)$ A

$$\mathbf{I}_y = 50\underline{/300^\circ} = 50\left(\frac{1}{2}-j\frac{\sqrt{3}}{2}\right) = 25(1-j\sqrt{3}) \text{ A}$$

$$\mathbf{I}_b = 30\underline{/180^\circ} = (-30+j0) \text{ A}$$

Now the positive sequence component of current in the R line

$$= \mathbf{I}_1 = \tfrac{1}{3}[\mathbf{I}_r+h\mathbf{I}_y+h^2\mathbf{I}_b]$$

$$= \frac{1}{3}\left[50\left(\sqrt{3}+j\right)+\left(-\frac{1}{2}+j\frac{\sqrt{3}}{2}\right)\left(25\right)\left(1-\sqrt{3}\right)\right.$$

$$\left.+\left(-\frac{1}{2}-j\frac{\sqrt{3}}{2}\right)\left(-30\right)\right]$$

$$= \tfrac{5}{3}[10\sqrt{3}+j10+5+j5\sqrt{3}+3+j3\sqrt{3}]$$

$$= \tfrac{5}{3}[25{\cdot}32+j23{\cdot}856]$$

$$= \tfrac{5}{3}\times 25{\cdot}32\times 1{\cdot}375\underline{/\tan^{-1} 0{\cdot}945}$$

$$= \underline{\underline{58\underline{/43^\circ{\cdot}24'} \text{ A}}} \quad \textit{Ans.}$$

The negative sequence component of current in the *R* line

$$= \mathbf{I}_2 = \tfrac{1}{3}[\mathbf{I}_r + h^2\mathbf{I}_y + h\mathbf{I}_b]$$

$$= \frac{1}{3}\left[50\left(\sqrt{3}+j\right)+\left(-\frac{1}{2}-j\frac{\sqrt{3}}{2}\right)\left(25\right)\left(1-j\sqrt{3}\right) + \left(-\frac{1}{2}+j\frac{\sqrt{3}}{2}\right)\left(-30\right)\right]$$

$$= \tfrac{5}{3}[10\sqrt{3}+j10-10+3-j3\sqrt{3}] = \tfrac{5}{3}[10{\cdot}32+j4{\cdot}8]$$

$$= \tfrac{5}{3}\times 10{\cdot}32\times 1{\cdot}11 \;\underline{/\tan^{-1} 0{\cdot}465}$$

$$= \underline{18{\cdot}9 \;/24^\circ{\cdot}56' \text{ A}} \quad \textit{Ans.}$$

The zero sequence component of current in the red line

$$= \mathbf{I}_0 = \tfrac{1}{3}[\mathbf{I}_r + \mathbf{I}_y + \mathbf{I}_b]$$

$$= \tfrac{1}{3}[50(\sqrt{3}+j)+25(1-j\sqrt{3})-30]$$

$$= \tfrac{1}{3}[81{\cdot}6+j6{\cdot}7]$$

$$= \tfrac{1}{3}[1+j0{\cdot}082]\times 81{\cdot}6 = 27{\cdot}2\underline{/\tan^{-1} 0{\cdot}082}$$

$$= \underline{27{\cdot}2/4^\circ{\cdot}41' \text{ A}} \quad \textit{Ans.}$$

Now return current in the neutral:

$$= \mathbf{I}_n = \mathbf{I}_r + \mathbf{I}_y + \mathbf{I}_b$$

$$= 3\mathbf{I}_0$$

$$= 81{\cdot}6+j6{\cdot}7$$

$$= \underline{81{\cdot}6/4^\circ{\cdot}41' \text{ A}} \quad \textit{Ans.}$$

6. The angular position of a flywheel, driven by an electric motor, is controlled from a handwheel employing a closed-loop automatic control system. The rotation of the moving parts is damped by viscous friction. Draw a block diagram and set up the differential equation of the system.

In a particular case the moment of inertia of the flywheel inclusive of that of the moving parts of the motor is 1,000 kg-m^2, the motor torque is 5,000 Nm per radian of misalignment, and the equivalent viscous frictional torque per unit angular velocity of the flywheel is 2,000 Nm per rad/sec, all referred to the output shaft. At time $t = 0$, with the equipment at rest, the handwheel is suddenly turned through an angle of 36°. Derive the equation of the subsequent angular position of the flywheel in relation to time and make a sketch of the form of this function.

Solution *Block diagram of a closed-loop automatic control system damped by viscous friction.*

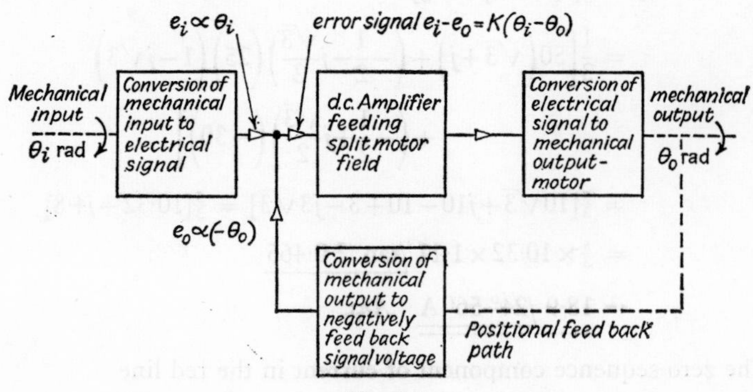

Fig. 3.5

The terms as in Paper No. IV—June 1961, question No. 7, page 61 should first be defined, and the equation of motion proven.

The equation of motion is:

$$J\frac{d^2\theta_o}{dt^2}+F\frac{d\theta_o}{dt}+K\theta_o = K\theta_i$$

In this case $J = 1000$ kg-m², $F = 2000$ Nm/rad/sec, $K = 5000$ Nm/rad, $\theta_i = 36\times\pi/180 = \pi/5$ rad.

$$\therefore\ 1000\frac{d^2\theta_o}{dt^2}+2000\frac{d\theta_o}{dt}+5000\,\theta_o = 5000\times\frac{\pi}{5}$$

$$\therefore\ \frac{d^2\theta_o}{dt^2}+2\cdot\frac{d\theta_o}{dt}+5\theta_o = \pi$$

By Laplace transforms,

$$s^2\bar{\theta}_o - s\theta_o(0) - \theta_o'(0) + 2s\bar{\theta}_o - 2\theta_o(0) + 5\bar{\theta}_o = \frac{\pi}{s}$$

The input being a step function.

When $t = 0$, $\theta_o = 0$

$$\therefore\ \theta_o(0) = 0$$

and when $t = 0$, $d\theta_o/dt = 0$

$$\therefore\ \theta_o'(0) = 0$$

$$\therefore\ \bar{\theta}_o(s^2+2s+5) = \frac{\pi}{s}$$

$$\therefore\ \bar{\theta}_o = \frac{\pi}{s[(s+1)^2+2^2]}$$

Consider

$$\mathscr{L}^{-1}\frac{1}{(s-1)(s^2+2^2)} = \frac{1}{5}\mathscr{L}^{-1}\frac{1^2+2^2}{(s-1)(s^2+2^2)}$$
$$= \tfrac{1}{5}(\varepsilon^t - \tfrac{1}{2}\sin 2t + \cos 2t)$$

$\therefore$ By means of the shifting theorem for s put $(s+1)$,

$$\therefore\ \theta_o = \mathscr{L}^{-1}\frac{\pi}{s[(s+1)^2+2^2]}$$
$$= \frac{\pi}{5}\varepsilon^{-t}\left(\varepsilon^t - \frac{1}{2}\sin 2t - \cos 2t\right)$$
$$= \frac{\pi}{5}\left[1 - \frac{1}{2}\varepsilon^{-t}(\sin 2t + 2\cos 2t)\right] \quad \textit{Ans.}$$

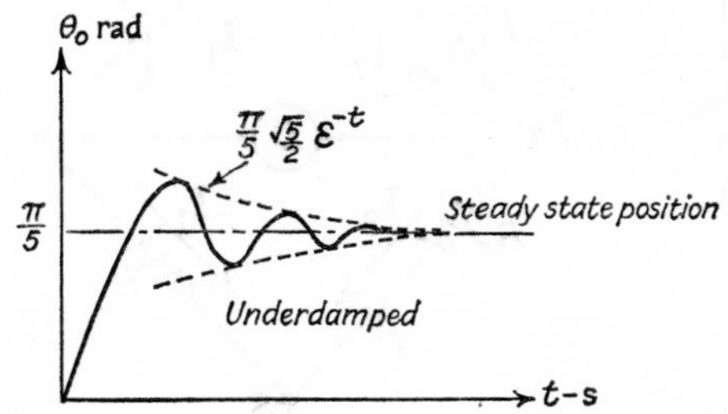

Fig. 3.6. Rough sketch of θ_0 with respect to time

$$\theta_o = \frac{\pi}{5}\left[1 - \varepsilon^{-t}\frac{1}{2}(\sin 2t + 2\cos 2t)\right]$$
$$= \frac{\pi}{5}\left[1 - \frac{\sqrt{5}}{2}\,\varepsilon^{-t}.\sin(2t+\alpha)\right] \quad \textit{Ans.}$$

where $\alpha = \tan^{-1} 2$.

PAPER NO. IV—JUNE, 1961

1. The a.c. bridge network shown below is used to measure the mutual inductance M. Derive the conditions required for balance.

What modification is required to make the balance independent of frequency? Draw the vector diagram for the bridge so modified, in its condition of balance.

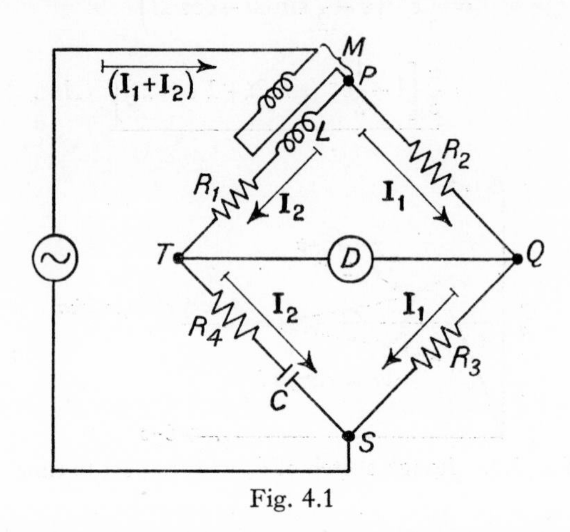

Fig. 4.1

Note: The conventional directions of current indicated were not shown in the original question.

Solution At balance, since the voltage across the detector is zero, then

$$\mathbf{V}_{PT} = \mathbf{V}_{PQ} \quad \text{and} \quad \mathbf{V}_{TS} = \mathbf{V}_{QS}$$

$$\therefore \; \mathbf{I}_2(R_1+j\omega L)+(\mathbf{I}_1+\mathbf{I}_2)j\omega M = \mathbf{I}_1 R_2 \tag{1}$$

and

$$\mathbf{I}_2\left(R_4-\frac{j}{\omega C}\right) = \mathbf{I}_1 R_3 \tag{2}$$

Substitute $\mathbf{I}_1$, obtained from equation (2), in equation (1).

$$\therefore \; \mathbf{I}_2(R_1+j\omega L)+\mathbf{I}_2\frac{j\omega M}{R_3}\left(R_4-\frac{j}{\omega C}\right)+\mathbf{I}_2\, j\omega M = \mathbf{I}_2\frac{R_2}{R_3}\left(R_4-\frac{j}{\omega C}\right)$$

$$\therefore \left(R_1+\frac{M}{CR_3}\right)+j\omega\left(L+M+M\frac{R_4}{R_3}\right) = \frac{R_2R_4}{R_3}-j\frac{R_2}{\omega CR_3}$$

Equating in phase components,

$$R_1+\frac{M}{CR_3} = \frac{R_2R_4}{R_3} \tag{3}$$

Equating in quadrature components,

$$\omega\left(L+M+M\frac{R_4}{R_3}\right) = -\frac{R_2}{\omega CR_3} \tag{4}$$

From equation (3),

$$M = C(R_2R_4-R_1R_3)\ \text{H} \tag{5}$$

From equation (4),

$$L+M\left(\frac{R_3+R_4}{R_3}\right) = -\frac{R_2}{\omega^2 CR_3}$$

$$\therefore\ M = -\left[\frac{R_2+\omega^2 CR_3L}{\omega^2 C(R_3+R_4)}\right]\ \text{H} \tag{6}$$

The mutual inductance M henrys may be found with the aid of equation (5) if C is a known standard capacitor, and the values of R_1, R_2, R_3, and R_4 are known. M may also be found with the aid of equation (6) if R_2, R_3, R_4, ω, C, and L are known. M found with the aid of equation (6) requires a knowledge of the frequency. *Equations (5) and (6) must be satisfied for balance conditions.*

In order to make the bridge independent of frequency put $R_2 = 0$.

$\therefore$ from equation (5) $\quad M = -R_1R_3C \qquad (7)$

and from equation (6) $\quad M = -\dfrac{R_3}{R_3+R_4}\cdot L \qquad (8)$

In order to satisfy equations 6, 7, and 8, M must be relatively negative; i.e. the coils of the mutual inductor must be wound in opposite directions so that the e.m.f. induced in the bridge circuit by virtue of the total current in the supply is $-j\omega M(\mathbf{I}_1+\mathbf{I}_2)$.

The original bridge is called the Carey Foster bridge, and the modification to make it independent of frequency is Heydweiller's modification.

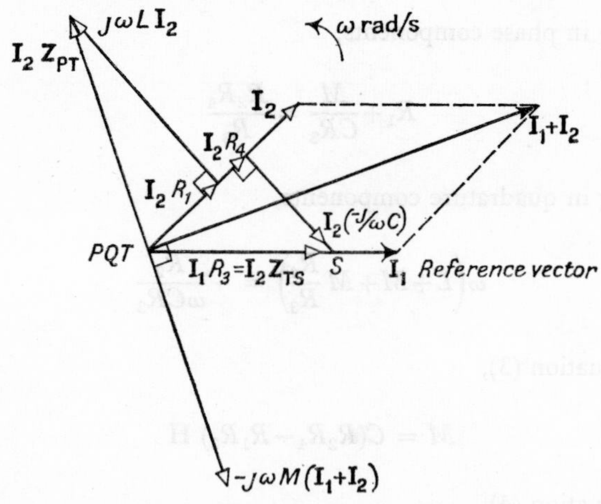

Fig. 4.2.—Vector diagram of the a.c. bridge at balance with $R_2 = 0$

Note: $\mathbf{V}_{PQ} = \mathbf{V}_{PT} = 0$ and since the bridge is balanced $\mathbf{V}_{TQ} = 0$.

2. Explain what is meant by harmonic resonance in a.c. circuits.

A current having an instantaneous value of $2(\sin \omega t + \sin 3\omega t)$ amperes is passed through a circuit which consists of a coil of resistance R and inductance L in series with a capacitor C. Derive an expression for the value of ω at which the r.m.s. circuit voltage is a minimum. Determine this voltage if the coil has inductance 0·1 H and resistance 150 Ω, and the capacitance is 10 μF. Determine also the circuit voltage at the fundamental resonant frequency.

Solution *Harmonic resonance,* sometimes called selective resonance, occurs when the *n*th harmonic component of a complex voltage waveform is in phase with the resulting *n*th harmonic component of current flowing through a circuit containing reactive impedances. Both the components of voltage and current will be at the same frequency.

In the case of a series circuit containing both inductance and capacitance, large currents may be produced at the resonant frequency, and large voltages may appear across both the inductor and capacitor. In the case of a parallel circuit containing both inductance and capacitance, the current taken from the supply may be a minimum at the resonant frequency, but the circulating current through the inductor and capacitor will be large. These facts may give rise to practical difficulties as far as voltage rating and current protection are concerned in circuits to which a complex waveform is applied.

Numerical portion

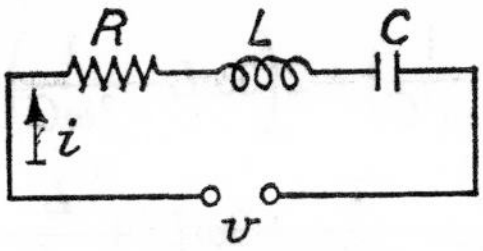

R L C
i
v

Fig. 4.3

Now $$i = 2(\sin \omega t + \sin 3\omega t) \text{ A}$$

The circuit impedance at the fundamental frequency

$$= Z_1 = \sqrt{R^2 + \left(\omega L - \frac{1}{\omega C}\right)^2} \ \Omega$$

The circuit impedance at the third harmonic component of frequency

$$= Z_3 = \sqrt{R^2 + \left(3\omega L - \frac{1}{3\omega C}\right)^2} \ \Omega$$

$\therefore$ The applied voltage waveform may be expressed as:

$$v = 2Z_1 \sin(\omega t + \phi_1) + 2Z_3 \sin(3\omega t + \phi_3) \text{ volts}$$
$$= V_{m1} \sin(\omega t + \phi_1) + V_{m3} \sin(3\omega t + \phi_3)$$

where

$$\phi_1 = \tan^{-1} \frac{\omega L - (1/\omega C)}{R} \quad \text{and} \quad \phi_3 = \tan^{-1} \frac{3\omega L - (1/3\omega C)}{R}$$

Now for a complex voltage waveform it may be shown from fundamental principles that the r.m.s. value of the waveform:

$$= V = \sqrt{\tfrac{1}{2}(V_{m1}{}^2 + V_{m3}{}^2)}$$

$$= \sqrt{\frac{1}{2} \cdot 4\left[R^2 + \left(\omega L - \frac{1}{\omega C}\right)^2 + R^2 + \left(3\omega L - \frac{1}{3\omega C}\right)^2\right.}$$

$$= \sqrt{2}\sqrt{2R^2 + \left(\omega L - \frac{1}{\omega C}\right)^2 + \left(3\omega L - \frac{1}{3\omega C}\right)^2}$$

Now for V to be a maximum or minimum

$$\frac{dV}{d\omega} = 0$$

Now $$\frac{dV}{d\omega} = \frac{2\left(\omega L - \frac{1}{\omega C}\right)\left(L + \frac{1}{\omega^2 C}\right) + 2\left(3\omega L - \frac{1}{3\omega C}\right)\left(3L + \frac{1}{3\omega^2 C}\right)}{\sqrt{2}\sqrt{2R^2 + \left(\omega L - \frac{1}{\omega C}\right)^2 + \left(3\omega L - \frac{1}{3\omega C}\right)^2}}$$

$\therefore$ Evidently for maximum or minimum value of V, ω is obtained from

$$2\left(\omega L-\frac{1}{\omega C}\right)\left(L+\frac{1}{\omega^2 C}\right)+2\left(3\omega L-\frac{1}{3\omega C}\right)\left(3L+\frac{1}{3\omega^2 C}\right)=0$$

$$\therefore\ \omega L^2+\frac{L}{\omega C}-\frac{L}{\omega C}-\frac{1}{\omega^3 C^2}+9\omega L^2+\frac{L}{\omega C}-\frac{L}{\omega C}-\frac{1}{9\omega^3 C^2}=0$$

$$\therefore\ \omega L^2=\frac{1}{9\omega^3 C^2}\qquad \therefore\ \omega^4=\frac{1}{9L^2C^2}$$

$$\therefore\ \omega=\frac{1}{\sqrt{3LC}}$$

By inspection of the voltage equation this is evidently the condition for V to be a minimum value.

Using this condition, and the given values of R, L, and C,

$$\therefore\ \omega=\frac{1}{\sqrt{3.10^{-1}\times 10.10^{-6}}}=\frac{10^3}{\sqrt{3}}\text{ rad/s}$$

$$\therefore\ \omega L=\frac{10^2}{\sqrt{3}};\qquad \frac{1}{\omega C}=\frac{\sqrt{3}}{10^3}\cdot\frac{10^6}{10}=\sqrt{3}.10^2$$

$$\left(\omega L-\frac{1}{\omega C}\right)=\frac{10^2}{\sqrt{3}}-\sqrt{3}.10^2=\frac{-2.10^2}{\sqrt{3}}$$

$$3\omega L=\frac{3.10^2}{\sqrt{3}};\qquad \frac{1}{3\omega C}=\frac{10^2}{\sqrt{3}}$$

$$\therefore\ \left(3\omega L-\frac{1}{3\omega C}\right)=\frac{2.10^2}{\sqrt{3}}$$

$$\therefore\ V=\sqrt{2}\cdot\sqrt{2\times 15^2.10^2+\frac{8}{3}.10^4}$$

$= \underline{378\text{ V}} =$ the minimum value of the applied voltage. *Ans.*

Now at the fundamental resonant frequency,

$$\omega_0=\frac{1}{\sqrt{LC}}=\frac{1}{\sqrt{10^{-1}\times 10^{-5}}}=10^3\text{ rad/s}$$

$$\omega_0 L-\frac{1}{\omega_0 C}=0\ \text{ and }\ \left(3\omega_0 L-\frac{1}{3\omega_0 C}\right)=3.10^2-\tfrac{1}{3}.10^2=\tfrac{8}{3}.10^2$$

$$\therefore\ V=\sqrt{2}\sqrt{2\times 15^2.10^2+(\tfrac{8}{3})^2.10^4}$$

$= \underline{483\text{ V}}$ *Ans.*

This value must be greater than the previous value.

3. Define the terms image impedance and iterative impedance as applied to 4-terminal networks. Calculate the iterative impedances for the network shown below. What is the insertion loss of the network when it is inserted between its iterative impedances?

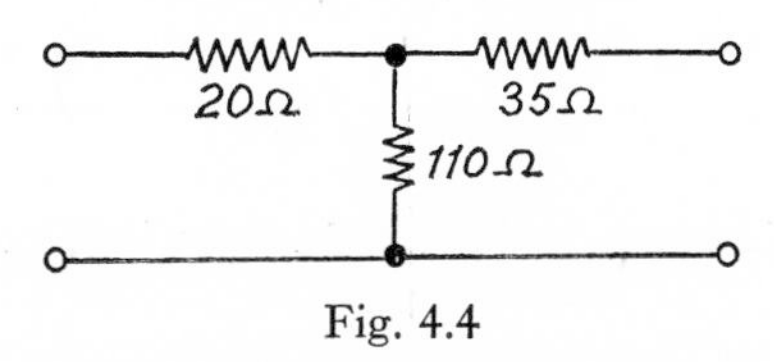

Fig. 4.4

Solution *Image impedances* of an asymmetrical quadripole linear passive network are defined as those impedances such that when one of them is connected across the appropriate pair of terminals, the other is presented by the other pair of terminals.

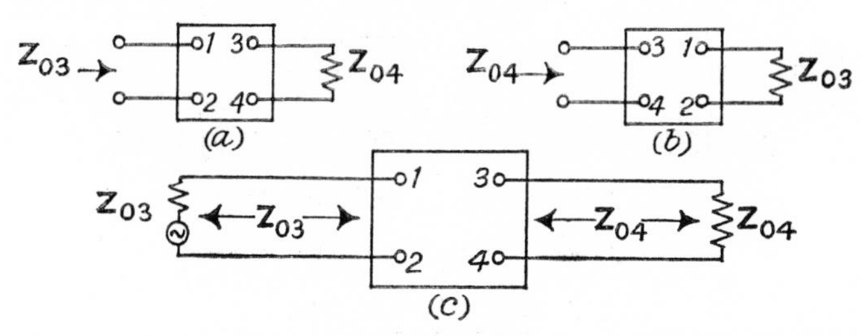

Fig. 4.5.—4-terminal network inserted between its image impedances

Iterative impedances of an asymmetrical quadripole linear passive network are defined as the input impedance measured at one pair of terminals when an infinite number of similar networks are connected in tandem. It may also be defined as the input impedance measured at one pair of terminals when the other pair of terminals are terminated with an impedance of the same value.

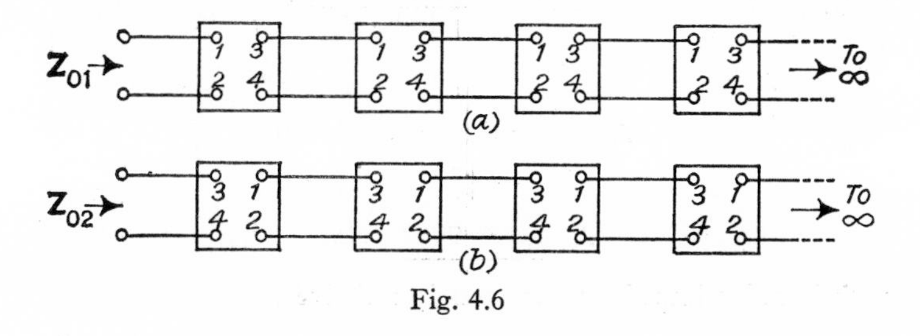

Fig. 4.6

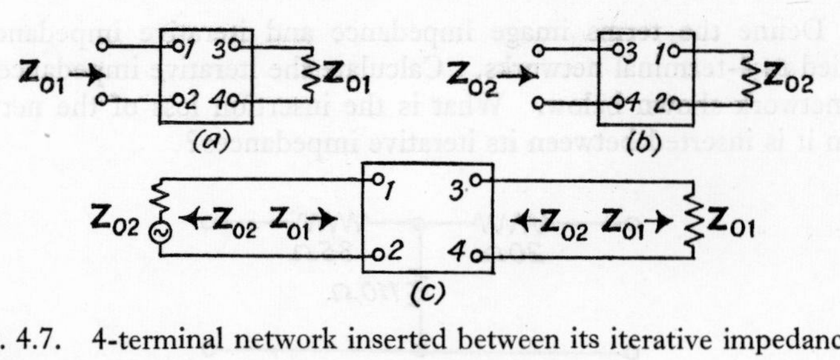

Fig. 4.7. 4-terminal network inserted between its iterative impedances.

Numerical portion

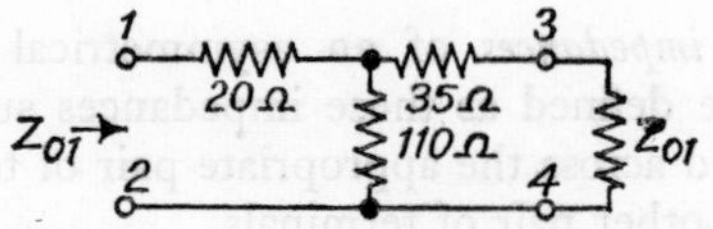

Fig. 4.8

By inspection $$Z_{01} = 20+\frac{110(35+Z_{01})}{145+Z_{01}}$$

$$\therefore\ 145\,Z_{01}+Z_{01}{}^{2} = 2900+20Z_{01}+3850+110Z_{01}$$

$$\therefore\ Z_{01}{}^{2}+15Z_{01}-6750 = 0$$

$$\therefore\ (Z_{01}+90)(Z_{01}-75) = 0$$

$$\therefore\ \underline{Z_{01} = 75\ \Omega} \quad \textit{Ans.}$$

Evidently Z_{02} should equal 90 Ω.

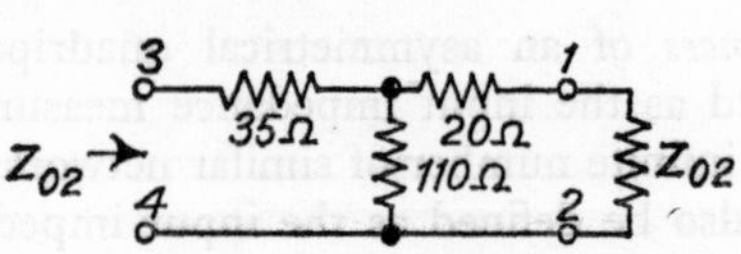

Fig. 4.9

By inspection $$Z_{02} = 35+\frac{110(20+Z_{02})}{130+Z_{02}}$$

$$\therefore\ 130Z_{02}+Z_{02}{}^{2} = 4550+35Z_{02}+2200+110Z_{02}$$

$$\therefore\ Z_{02}{}^{2}-15Z_{02}-6750 = 0$$

$$(Z_{02}-90)(Z_{02}+75) = 0$$

$$\therefore\ \underline{Z_{02} = 90\ \Omega} \quad \textit{Ans.}$$

Both iterative impedances are purely resistive.

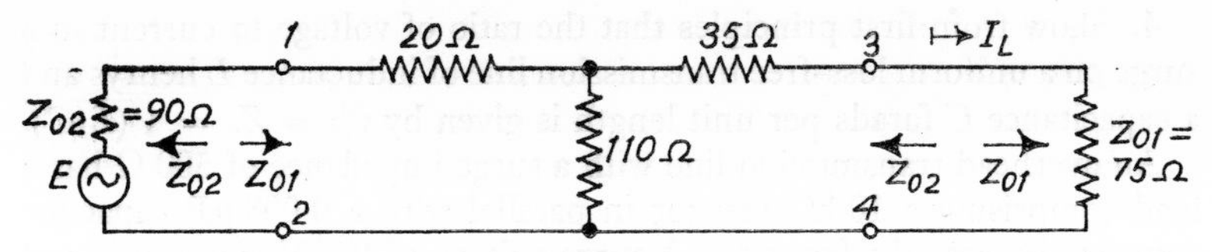

Fig. 4.10.—The given 4-terminal network inserted between its iterative impedances.

Note: If the generator of voltage E and the load are interchanged, then according to the Theorem of Reciprocity, the load current I_L will remain unchanged. Thus the insertion loss will be unchanged.

Before the insertion of the 4-terminal network

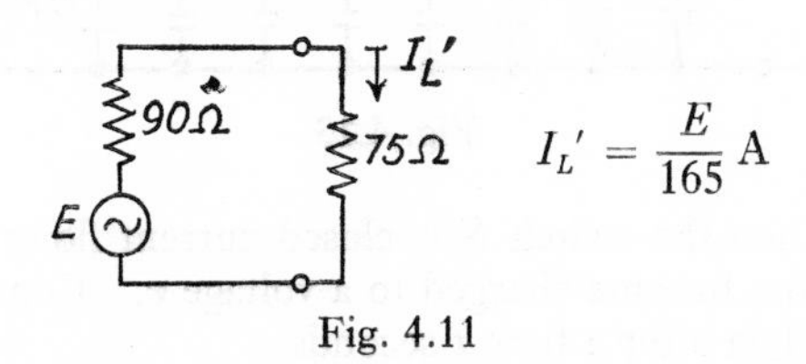

$$I_L' = \frac{E}{165} \text{ A}$$

Fig. 4.11

Using Thévenin's theorem to find I_L

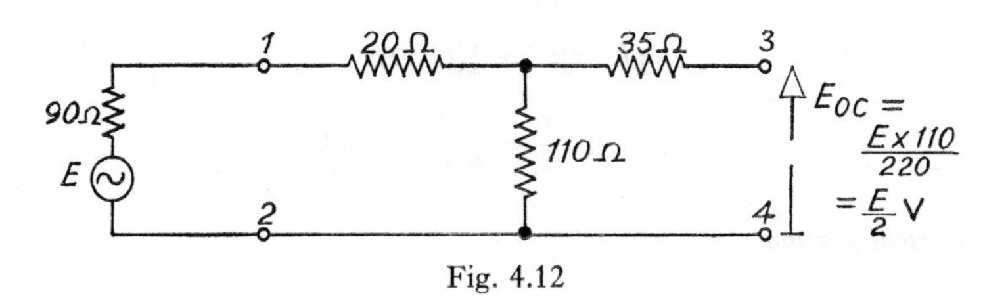

Fig. 4.12

The 'looking-in' impedance with the generator replaced by an impedance equal to its internal impedance $Z_{\text{in}} = Z_{02} = 90\ \Omega$, by definition.

$$\therefore\ I_L = \frac{E/2}{75+90} = \frac{E}{2 \times 165} \text{ A}$$

$\therefore$ By definition, insertion loss

$$= 20 \log I_L'/I_L = 20 \log \frac{E}{165} \times \frac{2 \times 165}{E}$$

$$= 20 \log 2$$

$$= \underline{6 \text{ db}} \quad \textit{Ans.}$$

4. Show from first principles that the ratio of voltage to current in a surge on a uniform loss-free transmission line of inductance L henrys and a capacitance C farads per unit length is given by $v/i = Z_0 = \sqrt{(L/C)}$.

An overhead transmission line with a surge impedance of 500 Ω has a load comprising a 10 kΩ resistor in parallel with a 0·005 μF capacitor connected across the far end. A surge voltage of 10 kV magnitude and unit function form travels along the line. Derive an expression for the time variation of the voltage across the load, and calculate this voltage 5 μs after the arrival of the wave front of the surge. State any assumptions made.

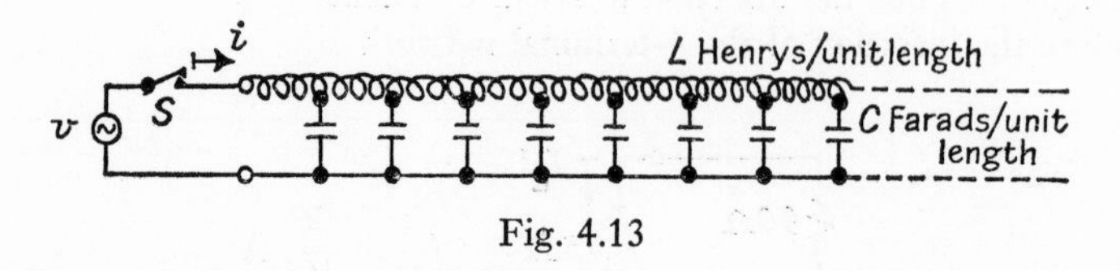

Fig. 4.13

Solution When the switch S is closed current flows along the line, and the capacitors become charged to a voltage v. Considering a small length line δx then after a time t seconds

energy given out by the inductors = energy stored by the capacitors

This assumes no loss along the line

$$\therefore \tfrac{1}{2}(L\,\delta x)i^2 = \tfrac{1}{2}(C\,\delta x)v^2$$

$$\therefore \frac{v}{i} = \sqrt{\frac{L}{C}} = Z_0\ \Omega$$

Numerical portion

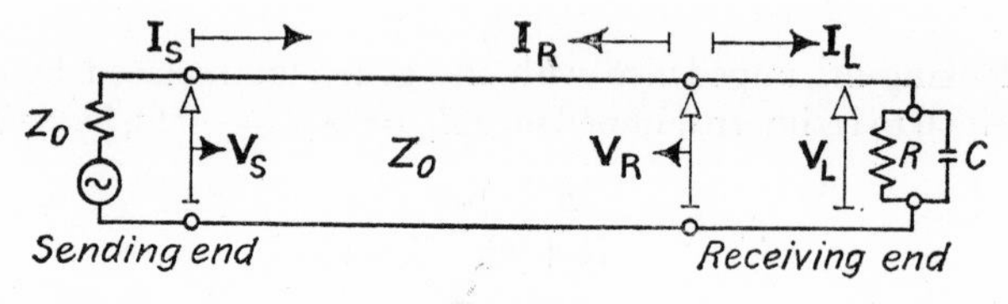

Fig. 4.14

Applying Kirchhoff's first and second laws at the junction of the transmission line and the termination,

$$\mathbf{I_S} = \mathbf{I_R} + \mathbf{I_L} \quad \text{where} \quad \mathbf{I_R} = \text{the reflected current}$$

$$\mathbf{V_S} + \mathbf{V_R} = \mathbf{V_L} \quad \text{where} \quad \mathbf{V_R} = \text{the reflected voltage}$$

Now, from the current equation,

$$\frac{\mathbf{V_S}}{Z_0} = \frac{\mathbf{V_R}}{Z_0} + \frac{\mathbf{V_L}}{\mathbf{Z_L}}$$

$$\therefore\ \mathbf{V_S} - \mathbf{V_R} = \frac{Z_0}{\mathbf{Z_L}} \cdot \mathbf{V_L} \tag{1}$$

Also

$$\mathbf{V_S} + \mathbf{V_R} = \mathbf{V_L} \tag{2}$$

Adding equations (1) and (2),

$$2\mathbf{V_S} = \mathbf{V_L}\left(1 + \frac{Z_0}{\mathbf{Z_L}}\right)$$

$$\therefore\ \mathbf{V_L} = \frac{2\mathbf{V_S}}{1 + \frac{Z_0}{\mathbf{Z_L}}} = \frac{2\mathbf{V_S}}{1 + \frac{Z_0[R + (1/pC)]}{R(1/pC)}} \quad \text{where } p = j\omega$$

$$= \frac{2R(1/pC)}{R(1/pC) + Z_0[R + (1/pC)]} \cdot \mathbf{V_S}$$

Taking Laplace transforms,

$$\bar{V}_L = \frac{2R(1/pC)}{R(1/pC) + Z_0[R + (1/pC)]} \cdot \frac{V_S}{p} \quad \text{since } \mathbf{V_S} \text{ is a unit function}$$

$$= \frac{2R(1/pC)}{p[Z_0 R + (1/pC)(R + Z_0)]} V_S$$

$$\therefore\ \bar{V}_L = \frac{2R/Z_0 RC}{p[p + (R + Z_0)/Z_0 RC]} \cdot V_S$$

$$= \frac{\frac{R + Z_0}{Z_0 RC} \cdot \frac{Z_0 RC}{R + Z_0} \cdot \frac{2R}{Z_0 RC} \cdot V_S}{p\left[p + \frac{R + Z_0}{Z_0 RC}\right]}$$

$\therefore$ From tables of inverse Laplace transforms,

$$V_L = \frac{2RV_S}{R + Z_0}[1 - \varepsilon^{-[(R + Z_0)/Z_0 CR]t}] \quad \textit{Ans.}$$

Given $V_S = 10$ kV; $R = 10$ kΩ; $Z_0 = 500$ Ω; $C = 0{\cdot}005 . 10^{-6}$ F; $t = 5 . 10^{-6}$ s,

$$\therefore\ V_L = \frac{2 . 10^4 \times 10}{10^4 + 5 . 10^2}[1 - \varepsilon^{-\left(\frac{10^4 + 5 . 10^2}{5 . 10^2 \times 0{\cdot}005 . 10^{-6} \times 10^4}\right)5 . 10^{-6}}] \text{ kV}$$

$$= 19{\cdot}1[1 - \varepsilon^{2{\cdot}1}] \text{ kV}$$

$$= 16{\cdot}6 \text{ kV} \quad \textit{Ans.}$$

Assumptions made:

1. The line is lossless.
2. The generator impedance is matched to the input impedance of the transmission line, which is terminated in a complex impedance; i.e. there are no reflections down the line, from the sending end.
3. The capacitor C is initially uncharged.

5. Two equal impedance arms AB and BC are connected to the terminals A, B, C of a 3-phase supply, as shown in Fig. 4.15. Each capacitor has a reactance of $X = \sqrt{3}R$. A high impedance voltmeter V is connected to the circuit at the points a and c as shown. If the supply line voltages V_{AB}, V_{BC}, V_{CA} are balanced, determine either algebraically or graphically the reading of the voltmeter (*a*) when the phase sequence of the supply voltages is *A-B-C*, and (*b*) when the phase sequence is reversed. Hence explain how the network could be employed to measure, respectively, the positive and negative phase sequence voltage components of an unbalanced 3-phase supply.

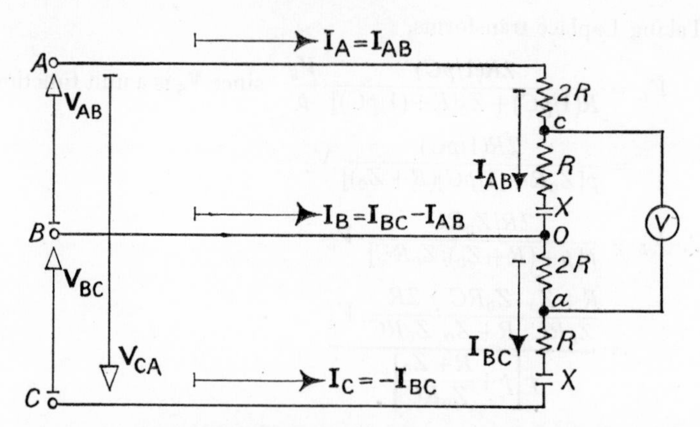

Fig. 4.15.—The conventional directions of voltage and current were not shown in the original question

Solution 1. Using the conventional directions of voltage and current as indicated in the diagram.

2. Choose $\mathbf{V_{AB}}$ as the reference vector

$$\therefore \mathbf{V_{AB}} = V(1+j0)$$

$$\mathbf{V_{BC}} = a^2V$$

$$\mathbf{V_{CA}} = aV$$

3. In the first instance phase sequence is ABC.

By inspection of the circuit diagram,

$$\mathbf{I}_{AB} = \frac{\mathbf{V}_{AB}}{3R-jX} = \frac{V}{3R-j\sqrt{3}R} = \frac{V}{\sqrt{3}R(\sqrt{3}-j)}\ \text{A}$$

$$\mathbf{I}_{BC} = \frac{\mathbf{V}_{BC}}{3R-jX} = \frac{a^2V}{\sqrt{3}R(\sqrt{3}-j)}\ \text{A}$$

Now evidently $\mathbf{V}_{cO}+\mathbf{V}_{Oa} = \mathbf{V}_{ca}$

$$\therefore\ \mathbf{V}_{ca} = \mathbf{I}_{AB}(R-jX)+\mathbf{I}_{BC}.2R$$

$$= \frac{V}{\sqrt{3}R(\sqrt{3}-j)}\cdot R(1-j\sqrt{3})+\frac{a^2V}{\sqrt{3}R(\sqrt{3}-j)}\cdot 2R$$

$$= \frac{V}{\sqrt{3}(\sqrt{3}-j)}\cdot(1-j\sqrt{3}+2a^2)\quad \text{where } a^2 = -\tfrac{1}{2}-j\frac{\sqrt{3}}{2}$$

$$= \frac{V}{\sqrt{3}(\sqrt{3}-j)}(-j2\sqrt{3})$$

$$\therefore\ |\mathbf{V}_{ca}| = \frac{V}{\sqrt{3}.2}\cdot 2\sqrt{3} = V \quad \textit{Ans.}$$

Since the voltmeter is not phase sensitive, with the phase sequence ABC it will read the magnitude of the line voltage.

In the second case, with sequence ACB,

$$\therefore\ \mathbf{V}_{AB} = V(1+j0), \text{ the reference vector}$$

$$\mathbf{V}_{BC} = aV$$

$$\mathbf{V}_{CA} = a^2V$$

As before $\mathbf{V}_{ca} = \mathbf{V}_{cO}+\mathbf{V}_{Oa}$

$$= \mathbf{I}_{AB}(R-jX)+\mathbf{I}_{BC}.2R$$

$$= \frac{V(R-jX)}{\sqrt{3}R(\sqrt{3}-j)}+\frac{aV.2R}{\sqrt{3}R(\sqrt{3}-j)}$$

$$= \frac{V}{\sqrt{3}(\sqrt{3}-j)}\cdot(1-j\sqrt{3}+2a)\quad \text{where } a = -\tfrac{1}{2}+j\frac{\sqrt{3}}{2}$$

$$= \frac{V}{\sqrt{3}(\sqrt{3}-j)}\cdot(1-j\sqrt{3}-1+j\sqrt{3}) = 0 \quad \textit{Ans.}$$

Hence with the phase sequence reversed the voltmeter reads zero.

Now the zero sequence components of the unbalanced applied voltages = $\mathbf{V}_0 = \frac{1}{3}[\mathbf{V}_{AB}+\mathbf{B}_{BC}+\mathbf{V}_{CA}] = 0$ since it is a 3-phase system.

The positive sequence component of the unbalanced line voltages = $\mathbf{V}_1 = \frac{1}{3}[\mathbf{V}_{AB}+a\mathbf{V}_{BC}+a^2\mathbf{V}_{CA}]$ which would be indicated on the voltmeter since it only reads with sequence *ABC*. Thus the voltmeter would read the full line voltage of the positive sequence component of the unbalanced line voltages.

The negative sequence component of the unbalanced line voltages = $\mathbf{V}_2 = \frac{1}{3}[\mathbf{V}_{AB}+a^2\mathbf{V}_{BC}+a\mathbf{V}_{CA}]$. This is not present in balanced line voltages. Thus if the sequence *ABC* is reversed the voltmeter will indicate the line voltage of the negative sequence component of the unbalanced supply voltages.

A rigid proof is as follows:

With the phase sequence *ABC*,

$$\mathbf{V}_{ca} = \frac{\mathbf{V}_{AB}}{3R-j\sqrt{3}R}\cdot(R-j\sqrt{3}R)+\frac{\mathbf{V}_{BC}}{3R-j\sqrt{3}R}\cdot 2R$$

$$= \frac{1}{3-j\sqrt{3}}[(\mathbf{V}_1+\mathbf{V}_2)(1-j\sqrt{3})+(a^2\mathbf{V}_1+a\mathbf{V}_2)2]$$

$$= \frac{1}{3-j\sqrt{3}}[\mathbf{V}_1(1-j\sqrt{3}+2a^2)+\mathbf{V}_2(1-j\sqrt{3}+2a)]$$

$$= \frac{1}{3-j\sqrt{3}}\cdot\mathbf{V}_1(-j2\sqrt{3})$$

since $a^2 = -\frac{1}{2}-j\frac{\sqrt{3}}{2}$ and $a = -\frac{1}{2}+j\frac{\sqrt{3}}{2}$

$\therefore\ |\mathbf{V}_{ca}| = |\mathbf{V}_1| =$ the positive phase sequence component, which is the voltmeter reading

With the phase sequence *ACB*,

$$\mathbf{V}_{ca} = \frac{1}{3-j\sqrt{3}}[(\mathbf{V}_1+\mathbf{V}_2)(1-j\sqrt{3})+(a\mathbf{V}_1+a^2\mathbf{V}_2)2]$$

$$= \frac{1}{3-j\sqrt{3}}[\mathbf{V}_1(1-j\sqrt{3}+2a)+\mathbf{V}_2(1-j\sqrt{3}+2a^2)]$$

$$= \frac{1}{3-j\sqrt{3}}[\mathbf{V}_2(-j2\sqrt{3})]$$

$\therefore\ |\mathbf{V}_{ca}| = |\mathbf{V}_2| =$ the negative phase sequence component, which is the voltmeter reading

6. Explain what is meant by amplitude modulation of a sine-wave carrier.

A signal voltage $v_1 = 2 \sin 157t$ and a carrier voltage $v_2 = 5 \sin 6280t$ are applied in series between the grid and cathode of a valve for which the anode current/grid voltage characteristic under the condition of operation is:

$$i_a = 6+2v_g+0{\cdot}1v_g^2$$

where i_a is in milliamperes and v_g is in volts.

Calculate (*a*) the frequency and amplitude of the various components of the anode current and (*b*) the depths of modulation produced. Roughly sketch the anode current waveform.

Solution The transmission of radio waves requires some means to control the radio waves by the desired intelligence. Normally information in the audio frequency range is required to be transmitted, hence the radio frequency waves transmitted must vary in accordance with the audio frequency waves of intelligence. This is called MODULATING

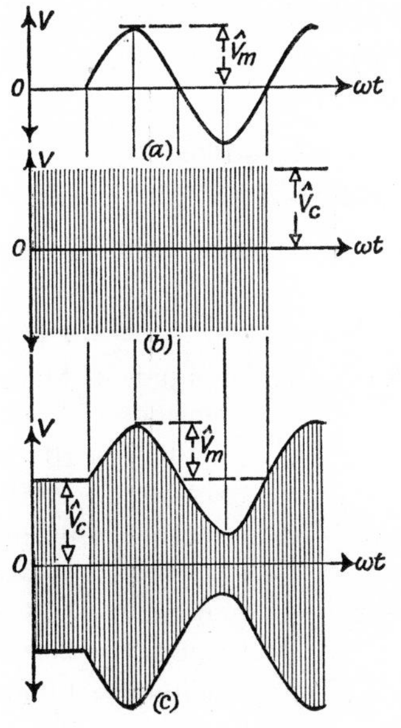

$v_m = \hat{V}_m \sin \omega_m t$ = *the modulating signal*

$v_c = \hat{V}_c \sin \omega_c t$ = *the carrier signal*

$$\omega_c > \omega_m$$

The modulated carrier wave

The amplitude of the modulation envelope

$$= (\hat{V}_c + \hat{V}_m \sin \omega_m t) \sin \omega_c t$$

$$= \hat{V}_c\left(1+\frac{\hat{V}_m}{\hat{V}_c} \sin \omega_m t\right) \sin \omega_c t$$

where $\hat{V}_m/\hat{V}_c = m$ = the depth of modulation usually expressed as a percentage.

In this case $m < 100\%$

Fig. 4.16

Note: In the limited time available to complete each question, approximately 35 minutes, the above facts would adequately show that the student has a thorough understanding of amplitude modulation.

the radio frequency wave in accordance with the intelligence. One of the methods of achieving this is called AMPLITUDE MODULATION, *where the frequency of the radio frequency carrier remains constant, and its amplitude varies according to the audio frequency intelligence to be transmitted.*

Now the grid-cathode voltage

$$v_g = v_1 + v_2$$

$$= 2 \sin 157t + 5 \sin 6280t$$

$$= 2 \sin 50\pi t + 5 \sin 2000\,\pi t \quad (1)$$

Given $$i_a = (6 + 2v_g + 0{\cdot}1v_g^2) \text{ mA} \quad (2)$$

Substitute equation (1) in equation (2).

$$\therefore\ i_a = 6 + 2(2 \sin 50\pi t + 5 \sin 2000\pi t) + 0{\cdot}1(2 \sin 50\pi t + 5 \sin 2000\pi t)^2$$

$$= 6 + 4 \sin 50\pi t + 10 \sin 2000\pi t + 0{\cdot}1(4 \sin^2 50\pi t + 20 \sin 50\pi t . \sin 2000\pi t + 25 \sin^2 2000\pi t)$$

$$= 6 + 4 \sin 50\pi t + 10 \sin 2000\pi t + 0{\cdot}4(\tfrac{1}{2})(1 - \cos 100\pi t) + 2(\tfrac{1}{2})(\cos 1950\pi t - \cos 2050\pi t) + 2{\cdot}5(\tfrac{1}{2})(1 - \cos 4000\pi t)$$

$$= (7{\cdot}45 + 4 \sin 50\pi t + 10 \sin 2000\pi t - 0{\cdot}2 \cos 100\pi t - 1{\cdot}25 \cos 4000\pi t + \cos 1950\pi t + \cos 2050\pi t) \text{ mA} \quad -(3)$$

By inspection of equation (3), the various components of anode current are:

1. Amplitude of the d.c. component $= 7{\cdot}45$ mA
2. Signal current component $= 4 \sin 50\pi t$ $\therefore$ Amplitude $= 4{\cdot}0$ mA, frequency $= 25$ c/s
3. Carrier current component $= 10 \sin 2000\pi t$ $\therefore$ Amplitude $= 10{\cdot}0$ mA, frequency $= 1000$ c/s
4. Second harmonic component of signal current $= -0{\cdot}2 \cos 100\pi t$ $\therefore$ Amplitude $= 0{\cdot}2$ mA, frequency $= 50$ c/s
5. Second harmonic component of carrier current $= -1{\cdot}25 \cos 4000\pi t$ $\therefore$ Amplitude $= 1{\cdot}25$ mA, frequency $= 2000$ c/s
6. Lower side band component $= \cos 1950\pi t$ $\therefore$ Amplitude $= 1{\cdot}0$ mA, frequency $= 975$ c/s
7. Upper side band component $= -\cos 2050\pi t$ $\therefore$ Amplitude $= 1{\cdot}0$ mA, frequency $= 1025$ c/s

$$\text{Depth of modulation of anode current} = \frac{2 \times I_{SB}}{I_c} = m_a$$

where I_{SB} = the r.m.s. value of the side band current either U.S.B. or L.S.B.

I_c = the r.m.s. value of the carrier current

$$\therefore\ m_a = \frac{2 \times 1}{10} \times 100\% = \underline{20\%} \quad \textit{Ans.}$$

$$\text{Depth of modulation of applied voltage} = \frac{V_m}{V_c} = m_v$$

where V_c = the r.m.s. value of the carrier voltage
V_m = the r.m.s. value of the modulating voltage

$$\therefore\ m_v = \tfrac{2}{5} \times 100 = \underline{40\%} \quad \textit{Ans.}$$

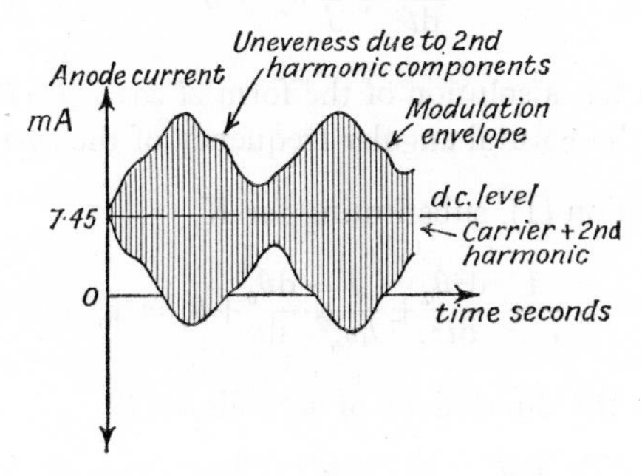

Fig. 4.17.—A rough sketch of the anode current waveform

7. A servo system for the positional control of a rotatable mass is stabilized by viscous damping which is less than that required for critical damping. Derive an expression for the output of the new system, initially at rest, if the input member is suddenly moved to a new position.

Calculate the amount of the first overshoot if the undamped natural frequency is 4 c/s and the viscous friction coefficient is one-quarter of that required for critical damping.

Solution Let

θ_i = the angular position of the input shaft in radians relative to some arbitrary reference,

θ_o = the angular position of the output shaft in radians relative to some arbitrary reference,

J = the moment of inertia of the output load, and all the moving parts in kg-m^2,

K = the torque in Nm/rad of misalignment between the input and output shaft, and

F = viscous friction damping coefficient in Nm/rad/sec.

Now the torque due to the acceleration of the output shaft plus the torque required to overcome viscous friction damping equals the torque due to the misalignment between the input and output shafts.

$$\therefore\ J\frac{d^2\theta_o}{dt^2}+F\frac{d\theta_o}{dt} = K(\theta_i-\theta_o)$$

$$\therefore\ J\frac{d^2\theta_o}{dt^2}+F\frac{d\theta_o}{dt}+K\theta_o = K\theta_i \qquad (1)$$

When there is no friction and $\theta_i = 0$,

$$\frac{d^2\theta_o}{dt^2}+\frac{K}{J}\theta_o = 0$$

This equation has a solution of the form $A\cos\omega_n t+B\sin\omega_n t$, where $\omega_n = \sqrt{K/J}$ = the natural angular frequency of the system.

$\therefore$ From equation (1), substituting for K,

$$\frac{1}{\omega_n^2}\cdot\frac{d^2\theta_o}{dt^2}+\frac{F}{J\omega_n^2}\cdot\frac{d\theta_o}{dt}+\theta_o = \theta_i$$

Now $F/J\omega_n^2$ has the dimensions of seconds $= T$

$$\therefore\ \frac{d^2\theta_o}{dt^2}+\omega_n^2T\frac{d\theta_o}{dt}+\omega_n^2\theta_o = \omega_n^2\theta_i$$

Taking Laplace transforms,

$$p^2\bar{\theta}_o-p\theta_o(0)-\theta_o'(0)+\omega_n^2Tp\bar{\theta}_o-\omega_n^2T\theta_o(0)$$
$$+\omega_n^2\bar{\theta}_o = \omega_n^2\frac{\theta_i}{p} \quad \text{for an input step}$$

When $t = 0$, $\theta_o = 0$, and $d\theta_o/dt = 0$,

$$\therefore\ \theta_o(0) = 0 \quad\text{and}\quad \theta_o'(0) = 0$$

$$\therefore\ \bar{\theta}_o(p^2+\omega_n^2Tp+\omega_n^2) = \omega_n^2\frac{\theta_i}{p}$$

$$\therefore\ \bar{\theta}_o = \frac{\omega_n^2\theta_i}{p\left[p^2+\omega_n(\omega_nT)p+\left(\frac{\omega_nT}{2}\right)^2\omega_n^2+\omega_n^2-\omega_n^2\left(\frac{\omega_nT}{2}\right)^2\right]}$$

$$= \frac{\omega_n^2\theta_i}{p[(p+\alpha\omega_n)^2+\{\sqrt{\omega_n^2(1-\alpha^2)}\}^2]} \quad \text{where } \alpha = \frac{\omega_nT}{2}$$

Consider

$$\mathscr{L}^{-1}\frac{1}{(p-\alpha\omega_n)[p^2+\{\sqrt{\omega_n^2(1-\alpha^2)}\}^2]}$$

$$=\frac{1}{\alpha^2\omega_n^2+\omega_n^2(1-\alpha^2)}\mathscr{L}^{-1}\frac{(-\alpha\omega_n)^2+\omega_n^2(1-\alpha^2)}{(p-\alpha\omega_n)[p^2+\{\sqrt{\omega_n^2(1-\alpha^2)}\}^2]}$$

$$=\frac{1}{\omega_n^2}\left[\varepsilon^{\alpha\omega_n t}-\frac{\alpha\omega_n}{\omega_n\sqrt{1-\alpha^2}}\cdot\sin(\sqrt{1-\alpha^2}\cdot\omega_n t)-\cos(\sqrt{1-\alpha^2}\cdot\omega_n t)\right]$$

Hence by means of the shifting theorem for p put $p+\alpha\omega_n$

$$\therefore\ \theta_o=\omega_n^2\theta_i\,\mathscr{L}^{-1}\frac{1}{p[(p+\alpha\omega_n)^2+\{\sqrt{\omega_n^2(1-\alpha^2)}\}^2]}$$

$$=\theta_i\,.\,\varepsilon^{-\alpha\omega_n t}\left[\varepsilon^{\alpha\omega_n t}-\frac{\alpha}{\sqrt{1-\alpha^2}}.\sin(\sqrt{1-\alpha^2}\,.\,\omega_n t)-\cos(\sqrt{1-\alpha^2}\,.\,\omega_n t)\right]$$

$$=\theta_i\left[1-\frac{\alpha\varepsilon^{-\alpha\omega_n t}}{\sqrt{1-\alpha^2}}.\sin(\sqrt{1-\alpha^2}\,.\,\omega_n t)-\varepsilon^{-\alpha\omega_n t}.\cos(\sqrt{1-\alpha^2}\,.\,\omega_n t)\right]$$

Now if the damping is small, $0<\omega_n T<2$

$$\therefore\ 0<\alpha<1$$

$\omega_n T=2$ being the condition for critical damping.

$$\therefore\ \theta_o=\theta_i\left[1-\frac{\varepsilon^{-\alpha\omega_n t}}{\sqrt{1-\alpha^2}}\left\{\alpha.\sin(\sqrt{1-\alpha^2}\,.\,\omega_n t)+(\sqrt{1-\alpha^2}).\cos(\sqrt{1-\alpha^2}\,.\,\omega_n t)\right\}\right]$$

$$=\theta_i\left[1-\frac{\varepsilon^{-\alpha\omega_n t}}{\sqrt{1-\alpha^2}}.\sin(\sqrt{1-\alpha^2}\,.\,\omega_n t+\phi)\right] \quad (2)$$

where $\phi=\tan^{-1}\dfrac{\sqrt{1-\alpha^2}}{\alpha}$.

Numerical portion

For critical damping $\omega_n T=2$.

In this case since the viscous friction coefficient is $\frac{1}{4}$ of that required for critical damping $\omega_n T=\frac{1}{2}$.

$$\therefore\ \alpha=\tfrac{1}{4}$$

By inspection of equation (2), first swing occurs when

$$\sin(\sqrt{1-\alpha^2}\,.\,\omega_n t+\phi) = -1 = \sin\frac{3\pi}{2}$$

$$\therefore \sqrt{1-\alpha^2}\,.\,\omega_n t+\phi = \frac{3\pi}{2}$$

$$\therefore \frac{\sqrt{15}}{4}\,\omega_n t+\tan^{-1}\sqrt{15} = \frac{3\pi}{2}$$

$$\frac{\sqrt{15}}{4}\,\omega_n t+75{\cdot}5^\circ\times\frac{\pi}{180^\circ} = \frac{3\pi}{2}$$

$$\omega_n t = \frac{4}{\sqrt{15}}\left(\frac{3\pi}{2}-1{\cdot}318\right) = 3{\cdot}5 \text{ (i.e. just } > \pi)$$

$$\therefore \theta_o = \theta_i\left[1+\frac{4}{\sqrt{15}}\,\varepsilon^{-3\cdot5/4}\right]$$

$$= \theta_i[1{\cdot}42] \text{ rad}$$

$\therefore$ Amount of first overshoot $= 1{\cdot}42\times$ input amplitude or

42% overshoot. *Ans.*

Note: Although f_n is given as 4 c/s, it is not required in this problem, unless the time at which the first swing occurs is required.

PAPER NO. V—NOVEMBER, 1961

1. Explain what is meant by the terms nominal-π and equivalent-π when applied to a uniform transmission line.

Determine from first principles the values of the elements of an equivalent-π section for a transmission line having a characteristic impedance Z_0 and a propagation coefficient γ.

Solution *The nominal-π* is a quadripole network which approximately represents a uniform transmission line at one frequency. It is assumed that the distributed constants of the transmission line may be directly replaced by the lumped passive elements in the nominal-π network. Knowing the receiving end voltage, current, and power factor, the approximate values of the sending end voltage, current and power factor, may be calculated with the aid of this nominal-π network. It is normally assumed that the leakage resistance of the uniform transmission line is infinite, thus the shunt conductance G mho is zero.

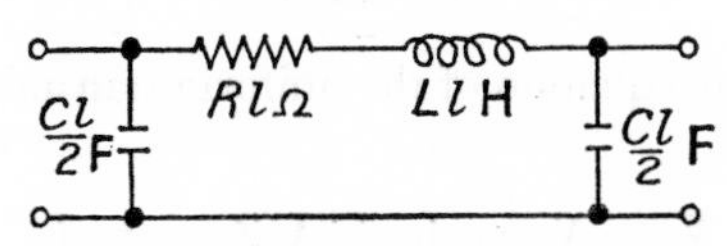

Fig. 5.1.—The nominal-π network

For the uniform transmission line:

R = the resistance per unit length in Ω,
L = the inductance per unit length in H,
C = the capacitance per unit length in F, and
l = the total length of the line.

The equivalent-π is a quadripole network which exactly represents a uniform transmission line at one particular frequency. Knowing the receiving end voltage, current, and power factor, the exact values of the sending end voltage, current, and power factor may be calculated with the aid of the equivalent-π network. It is not assumed that the distributed constants of the uniform transmission line may be directly replaced by lumped passive elements. The elements of the equivalent-π network are found by means of equating circuit conditions to the general line equations.

Determination from first principles of the values of the elements of an equivalent-π network to represent exactly a given length of uniform transmission line.

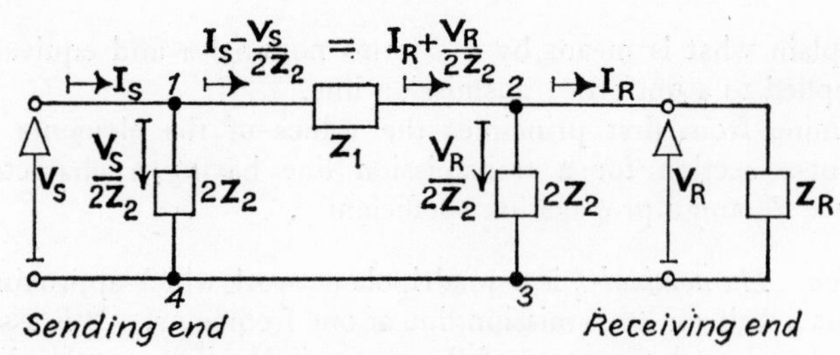

Fig. 5.2.—The equivalent π-network

Applying Kirchhoff's second law to the closed mesh 1 2 3 4,

$$\mathbf{V_S} = \left(\mathbf{I_R} + \frac{\mathbf{V_R}}{2\mathbf{Z}_2}\right)\mathbf{Z}_1 + \mathbf{V_R}$$

$$= \mathbf{V}_R\left(1 + \frac{\mathbf{Z}_1}{2\mathbf{Z}_2}\right) + \mathbf{I}_R\mathbf{Z}_1 \tag{1}$$

The general voltage equation of the uniform transmission line is of the form:

$$\mathbf{V_S} = \mathbf{V_R} \cosh \gamma l + \mathbf{I_R}\mathbf{Z}_0 \sinh \gamma l \tag{2}$$

where $\mathbf{Z}_0$ = the characteristic impedance,

γ = the propagation coefficient, and

l = the total length of the line.

Since the quadripole network is to exactly represent the uniform transmission line, then the coefficients of $\mathbf{V_R}$ and $\mathbf{I_R}$ contained in equations (1) and (2) may be equated.

$$\therefore \cosh \gamma l = \left(1 + \frac{\mathbf{Z}_1}{2\mathbf{Z}_2}\right) \tag{3}$$

and

$$\mathbf{Z}_1 = \mathbf{Z}_0 \sinh \gamma l \tag{4}$$

$\therefore$ from equation (3) $\quad 2\mathbf{Z}_2 = \dfrac{\mathbf{Z}_1}{\cosh \gamma l - 1}$

$$= \mathbf{Z}_0 \frac{\sinh \gamma l}{\cosh \gamma l - 1}$$

$$= \mathbf{Z}_0 \frac{2 \sinh \frac{\gamma l}{2} \cdot \cosh \frac{\gamma l}{2}}{2 \sinh^2 \frac{\gamma l}{2}}$$

$$= \frac{\mathbf{Z}_0}{\tanh \frac{\gamma l}{2}}$$

Hence, the series element

$$= \mathbf{Z}_1 = \mathbf{Z}_0 \sinh \gamma l \quad \textit{Ans.}$$

and each of the shunt elements

$$= 2\mathbf{Z}_2 = \frac{\mathbf{Z}_0}{\tanh \frac{\gamma l}{2}} \quad \textit{Ans.}$$

2. The bridge shown in Fig. 5.3 is used to measure a capacitor represented by a capacitance C_x and a dielectric loss resistance R_x.

Derive from the balance equations for the bridge an expression for C_x and the loss angle if balance is obtained at 400 c/s with $C_2 = C_3 = 0{\cdot}01\,\mu$F, $R_3 = 4{\cdot}0$ kΩ and $R_4 = 11{\cdot}5$ kΩ. Draw a vector diagram for the bridge in its balanced condition.

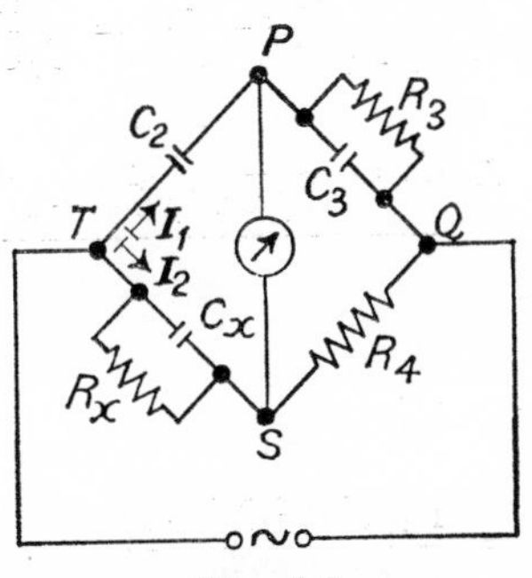

Fig. 5.3

Note: The conventional directions of current were not indicated in the figure given in the original question.

Solution At balance,

$$\mathbf{V}_{TP} = \mathbf{V}_{TS} \quad \text{and} \quad \mathbf{V}_{PQ} = \mathbf{V}_{SQ}$$

$$\therefore \mathbf{I}_1\mathbf{Z}_{TP} = \mathbf{I}_2\mathbf{Z}_{TS} \quad \text{and} \quad \mathbf{I}_1\mathbf{Z}_{PQ} = \mathbf{I}_2\mathbf{Z}_{SQ}$$

$$\therefore \mathbf{Z}_{TP}\,.\,\mathbf{Z}_{SQ} = \mathbf{Z}_{TS}\,.\,\mathbf{Z}_{PQ}$$

$$\therefore \frac{-j}{\omega C_2}\cdot R_4 = \left[\frac{R_x\left(\frac{-j}{\omega C_x}\right)}{R_x-\frac{j}{\omega C_x}}\right]\left[\frac{R_3\left(\frac{-j}{\omega C_3}\right)}{R_3-\frac{j}{\omega C_3}}\right]$$

$$\therefore (-j)\frac{R_4}{\omega C_2}\left[\left(R_xR_3-\frac{1}{\omega^2 C_x C_3}\right)-j\left(\frac{R_x}{\omega C_3}+\frac{R_3}{\omega C_x}\right)\right] = -\frac{R_xR_3}{\omega^2 C_x C_3} \quad (1)$$

$\therefore$ equating in-phase components of equation (1),

$$\frac{R_xR_3}{\omega^2 C_x C_3} = \frac{R_4}{\omega C_2}\left(\frac{R_x}{\omega C_3}+\frac{R_3}{\omega C_x}\right) \quad (2)$$

and equating in-quadrature components of equation (1),

$$R_xR_3-\frac{1}{\omega^2 C_x C_3} = 0 \quad (3)$$

From equation (2),

$$\frac{R_x}{C_3}\left(\frac{R_3}{C_x}-\frac{R_4}{C_2}\right) = \frac{R_3R_4}{C_2C_x} \quad (4)$$

Substitute for R_x, from equation (3), in equation (4),

$$\frac{1}{\omega^2 C_x C_3{}^2 R_3}\left(\frac{R_3}{C_x}-\frac{R_4}{C_2}\right) = \frac{R_3R_4}{C_2C_x}$$

$$\therefore C_x = \frac{R_3C_2}{R_4(\omega^2R_3{}^2C_3{}^2+1)} \quad \textit{Ans.} \quad (5)$$

From equation (3),

$$R_x = \frac{1}{\omega^2 C_x C_3 R_3}$$

$$= \frac{R_4(\omega^2R_3{}^2C_3{}^2+1)}{\omega^2C_3R_3{}^2C_2}$$

$$= R_4\left(\frac{C_3}{C_2}+\frac{1}{\omega^2C_2C_3R_3{}^2}\right) \quad (6)$$

Now, using the figures given,

$$\omega^2C_2C_3R_3{}^2 = (2\pi\times 400)^2\times(0{\cdot}01\times 10^{-6})^2\times(4\times 10^3)^2$$

$$= 64\times 16\times\pi^2\times 10^{-6}$$

$$= 0{\cdot}0101 \quad \text{which is} < 1{\cdot}0$$

∴ From equation (5), to slide-rule accuracy,

$$C_x = \frac{R_3}{R_4} \cdot C_2 \tag{7}$$

and from equation (6), since $C_2 = C_3$ and $1/\omega^2 C_2 C_3 R_3^2 > 1{\cdot}0$,

$$R_x = \frac{R_4}{\omega^2 C_2 C_3 R_3^2} \tag{8}$$

The loss angle is obtained by means of the vector diagram of the loss-free capacitor C_x in parallel with the resistor R_x which represents the losses.

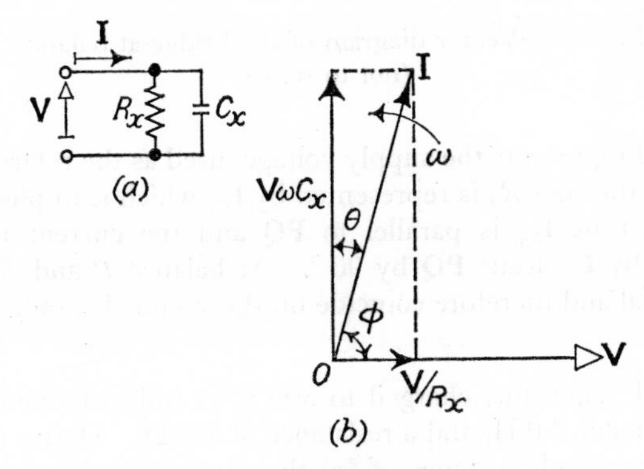

Fig. 5.4

$$\begin{aligned}
\text{Loss angle} &= \cos\phi = \sin\theta \\
&\simeq \tan\theta \quad \text{if } \theta \text{ is small} \\
&= \frac{1}{\omega C_x R_x} \\
&= \frac{R_4 \omega^2 C_2 C_3 R_3^2}{\omega R_3 C_2 R_4} \\
&= \omega C_3 R_3
\end{aligned} \tag{9}$$

Using the figures given:

$$C_x = \frac{4}{11{\cdot}5} \times 0{\cdot}01\ \mu\text{F} = 0{\cdot}00348\ \mu\text{F}$$

$$R_x = \frac{11{\cdot}4 \times 10^{12}}{(2\pi \times 400)^2 \times (0{\cdot}01)^2 \times (4.10^3)^2} = 1140\ \text{k}\Omega$$

$$\text{loss angle} = 2\pi \times 400 \times 0{\cdot}01 \times 10^{-6} \times 4 \times 10^3 = \underline{0{\cdot}101} \quad \textit{Ans.}$$

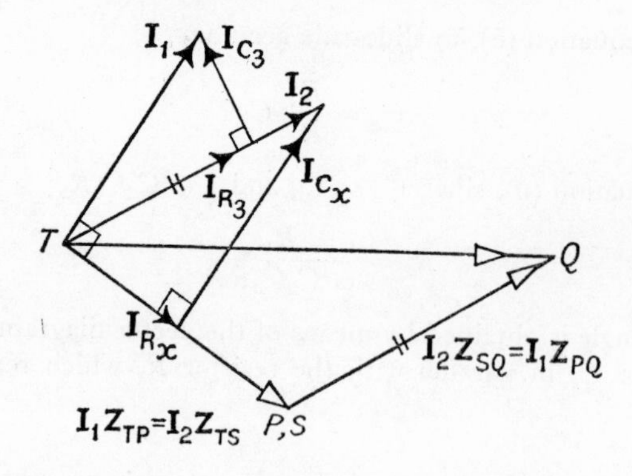

Fig. 5.5—Vector diagram of the bridge at balance (not to scale)

Vector **TQ** represents the supply voltage, used as the reference vector. The current through R_3 is represented by $\mathbf{I}_{R_3}$ which is in phase with the voltage **PQ**, thus $\mathbf{I}_{R_3}$ is parallel to **PQ** and the current through C_3 represented by $\mathbf{I}_{C_3}$ leads **PQ** by 90 °. At balance P and S are at the same potential and therefore coincide on the vector diagram.

3. A 50 μF capacitor, charged to 300 V, is suddenly connected to a coil of inductance 2·0 H, and a resistance of 500 Ω. Derive expressions for, and draw rough sketches of (*a*) the capacitor voltage, and (*b*) the current in the circuit subsequent to the connection. Calculate also the time at which the current reaches its maximum value.

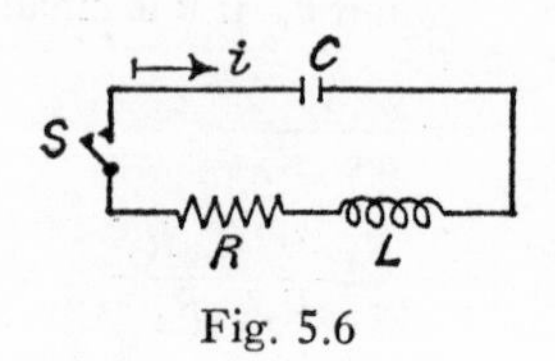

Fig. 5.6

Solution Applying Kirchhoff's second law to the network,

$$L\frac{\mathrm{d}i}{\mathrm{d}t}+Ri+\frac{q}{C} = 0 \qquad (1)$$

where i is the instantaneous value of the current at any time t seconds after closing the switch S, and q is the instantaneous value of the charge in coulombs, on the capacitor.

By fundamental definition,

$$\frac{dq}{dt} = i \qquad \therefore \frac{d^2q}{dt^2} = \frac{di}{dt}$$

$\therefore$ from equation (1),

$$L\frac{d^2q}{dt^2} + R\frac{dq}{dt} + \frac{q}{C} = 0$$

Now given $L = 2{\cdot}0$ H, $R = 500\ \Omega$, $C = 50.10^{-6}$ F,

$$\therefore 2\frac{d^2q}{dt^2} + 500\frac{dq}{dt} + 2.10^4 q = 0$$

$$\therefore \frac{d^2q}{dt^2} + 250.\frac{dq}{dt} + 10^4 q = 0$$

Taking Laplace transforms,

$$s^2\bar{q} - sq(0) - q'(0) + 250s\bar{q} - 250q(0) + 10^4\bar{q} = 0$$

$$\therefore \bar{q}(s^2 + 250s + 10^4) = sq(0) + q'(0) + 250q(0) \qquad (2)$$

when $t = 0$, $q = CV = 50.10^{-6} \times 300 = 15.10^{-3} = q(0)$

also when $t = 0$, $\frac{dq}{dt} = i = 0 \quad \therefore q'(0) = 0$

$\therefore$ From equation (2),

$$\bar{q}(s+50)(s+200) = 15.10^{-3}(s+250)$$

$$\therefore \bar{q} = 15.10^{-3}.\frac{(s+200)+50}{(s+50)(s+200)}$$

$$= 15.10^{-3}\left[\frac{1}{(s+50)} + \frac{50}{150}\cdot\frac{200-50}{(s+200)(s+50)}\right]$$

From the table of inverse Laplace transforms,

$$q = 15.10^{-3}[\varepsilon^{-50t} + \tfrac{1}{3}(\varepsilon^{-50t} - \varepsilon^{-200t})]$$

$$= 5.10^{-3}(4\varepsilon^{-50t} - \varepsilon^{-200t}) \text{ coulomb}$$

The instantaneous value of the capacitor voltage

$$v = \frac{q}{C} = \frac{5.10^{-3}}{50.10^{-6}}(4\varepsilon^{-50t} - \varepsilon^{-200t})$$

$$= 100(4\varepsilon^{-50t} - \varepsilon^{-200t}) \text{ V} \quad \textit{Ans. (a)}$$

Now $$\frac{dq}{dt} = i = 5.10^{-3}(-200\varepsilon^{-50t} + 200\varepsilon^{-200t})$$

$$= (\varepsilon^{-200t} - \varepsilon^{-50t}) \text{ A} \quad \textit{Ans. (b)}$$

Now $di/dt = -200\varepsilon^{-200t} + 50\varepsilon^{-50t} = 0$ for maximum or minimum value of the current.

$$\therefore 4 = \varepsilon^{150t}$$

$$\therefore t = \frac{1}{150}.\ln 4 = 9{\cdot}25 \text{ ms} \quad \textit{Ans.}$$

Evidently when $t = 9{\cdot}25$ ms, the current has its maximum magnitude, since when $t = 0$, the current is a minimum value of OA.

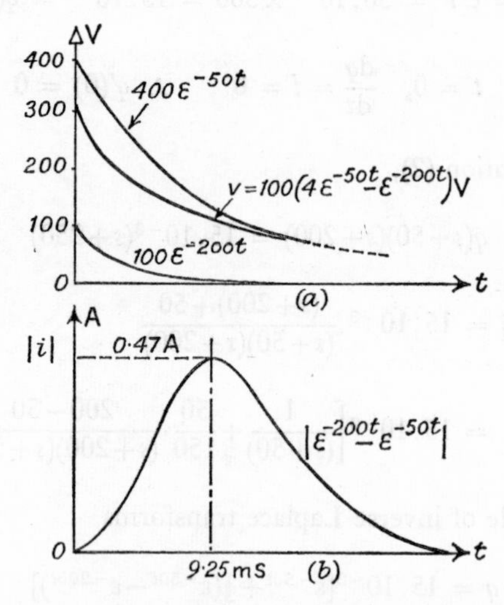

Fig. 5.7.—Sketches (not drawn to scale) of voltage, across the capacitor, and magnitude of current in the given circuit

4. Derive an expression for the ratio V_{out}/V_{in} for the network shown in Fig. 5.8, and show that at a certain frequency the output voltage is zero. Determine this frequency if C is 0·05 μF, and the inductance of the coil is 150 mH.

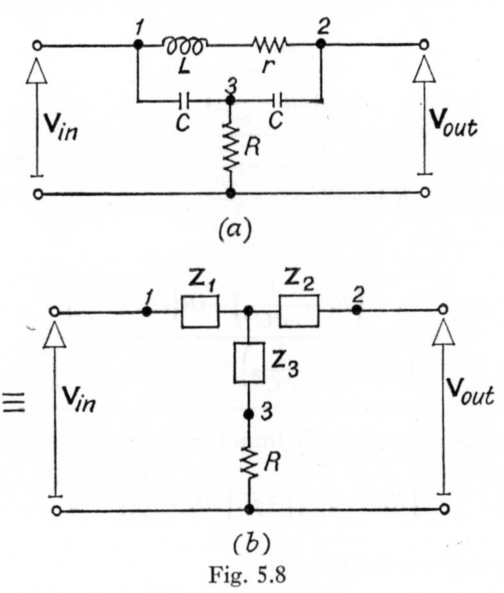

Fig. 5.8

Solution By delta to star conversion between the junctions 1, 2, 3,

$$\mathbf{Z}_1 = \frac{\left(r+j\omega L\right)\left(-\dfrac{j}{\omega C}\right)}{r+j\left(\omega L-\dfrac{2}{\omega C}\right)} = \mathbf{Z}_2$$

$$\therefore\ \mathbf{Z}_1 = \mathbf{Z}_2 = \frac{\dfrac{L}{C}-j\dfrac{r}{\omega C}}{r+j\left(\omega L-\dfrac{2}{\omega C}\right)} \tag{1}$$

and

$$\mathbf{Z}_3 = \frac{\left(\dfrac{-j}{\omega C}\right)\left(\dfrac{-j}{\omega C}\right)}{r+j\left(\omega L-\dfrac{2}{\omega C}\right)}$$

$$= \frac{-\dfrac{1}{\omega^2 C^2}}{r+j\left(\omega L-\dfrac{2}{\omega C}\right)} \tag{2}$$

Now by inspection of Fig. 5.8*b*

$$\frac{\mathbf{V}_{out}}{\mathbf{V}_{in}} = \frac{R+\mathbf{Z}_3}{R+\mathbf{Z}_1+\mathbf{Z}_3}$$

$$= \frac{R - \dfrac{\dfrac{1}{\omega^2 C^2}}{r+j\left(\omega L - \dfrac{2}{\omega C}\right)}}{R + \dfrac{\dfrac{L}{C} - \dfrac{1}{\omega^2 C^2} - j\dfrac{r}{\omega C}}{r+j\left(\omega L - \dfrac{2}{\omega C}\right)}}$$

$$= \frac{\left(Rr - \dfrac{1}{\omega^2 C^2}\right) + jR\left(\omega L - \dfrac{2}{\omega C}\right)}{\left(Rr + \dfrac{L}{C} - \dfrac{1}{\omega^2 C^2}\right) + j\left(\omega LR - \dfrac{2R}{\omega C} - \dfrac{r}{\omega C}\right)} \quad \textit{Ans.}$$

For V_{out} to be zero evidently from the above equation,

$$\left(Rr - \frac{1}{\omega^2 C^2}\right) + jR\left(\omega L - \frac{2}{\omega C}\right) = 0$$

∴ equating in phase components,

$$Rr = \frac{1}{\omega^2 C^2} \qquad (3)$$

and equating quadrature components,

$$\omega L = \frac{2}{\omega C} \qquad (4)$$

Both the conditions given by equations (3) and (4) must be satisfied if the output voltage is to be zero. Equation (4) gives the required frequency, and equation (3) must hold in order to make the impedance of the shunt path, consisting of $\mathbf{Z}_3$ in series with R, zero, i.e. from equation (2) $\mathbf{Z}_3 = -Rr/r = -R$

$$\therefore \ \mathbf{Z}_3 + R = 0$$

From equation (4),

$$\omega = \sqrt{\frac{2}{LC}} = \sqrt{\frac{2\times 10^6}{150.10^{-3}\times 0{\cdot}05}} = 10^4 \times 1{\cdot}64$$

$$\therefore \ \text{frequency} = \frac{\omega}{2\pi} = \underline{2{\cdot}60 \text{ kc/s}} \quad \textit{Ans.}$$

5. Explain what is meant by a standing wave on a transmission line, and state the conditions which give rise to it.

A coaxial air-insulated cable has a characteristic impedance of 100 Ω and negligible loss. A 60-metre length of this cable has one end open-circuited and the other end connected to a 5 Mc/s generator with an e.m.f. of 50 V and an internal impedance of $(100+j200)$ Ω. A non-reactive load of 100 Ω is connected across the cable at its mid-point. Calculate the steady state alternating current in the load.

Solution For the definition of standing wave see Paper No. VI—June 1962, question No. 6, page 90. The conditions that give rise to standing waves are when the terminating impedance of a uniform transmission line is not equal to its characteristic impedance, i.e. mismatch of the uniform transmission line.

For a loss-free transmission, which has a purely resistive characteristic impedance, the terminating impedance should also be of the same value and purely resistive to prevent the formation of standing waves. At radio frequencies the terminating resistor may have small values of series and shunt capacity, which can cause a mismatch of the transmission line. In practice it is only possible to match a transmission system at one frequency.

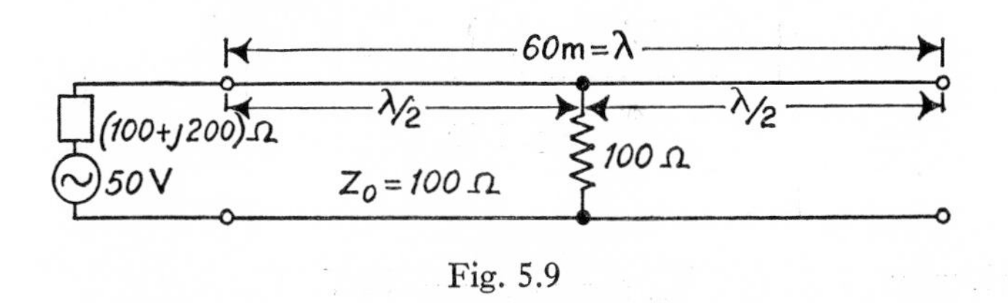

Fig. 5.9

Assuming the coaxial cable to be loss-free, the velocity of propagation is the same as the velocity of propagation of electromagnetic waves in free space:

$$c = 3.10^8 \text{ m/s} = f\lambda = 5.10^6\ \lambda$$

$$\therefore\ \lambda = \frac{3.10^8}{5.10^6} = 60 \text{ m} = \text{the wavelength}$$

Now the input impedance of a loss-free transmission line, or coaxial cable

$$= \mathbf{Z}_{\text{in}} = \mathbf{Z}_0\left[\frac{\mathbf{Z}_\mathbf{R}+j\mathbf{Z}_0 \tan \beta l}{\mathbf{Z}_0+j\mathbf{Z}_\mathbf{R} \tan \beta l}\right]$$

with the conventional notation of symbols.

Let $l = \lambda/2$

$$\therefore \mathbf{Z}_{in} = \mathbf{Z}_0\left[\frac{\mathbf{Z}_R + j\mathbf{Z}_0 \tan \frac{2\pi}{\lambda}\cdot\frac{\lambda}{2}}{\mathbf{Z}_0 + j\mathbf{Z}_R \tan \frac{2\pi}{\lambda}\cdot\frac{\lambda}{2}}\right] \quad \text{since } \beta\lambda = 2\pi \text{ by definition}$$

$$= \mathbf{Z}_R = \text{the terminating impedance, since } \tan\pi = 0$$

Thus the input impedance of a uniform transmission line, which is loss-free, and of electrical length $\lambda/2$, is equal to the terminating impedance. The voltage at the termination will have however, a phase change of π radians with respect to the sending end voltage.

In this question the $\lambda/2$ length of line to the right of the 100 Ω load, will have no effect upon the current flowing in the load, since its input impedance will be an open-circuit, i.e. $\mathbf{Z}_{in} = \mathbf{Z}_R = \infty$.

The original circuit may now be considered as:

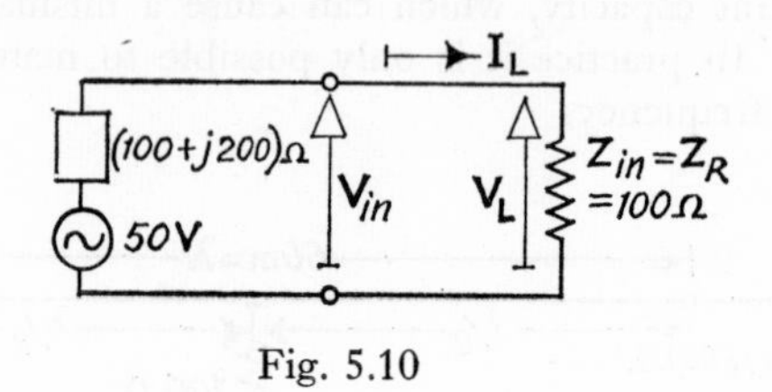

Fig. 5.10

Evidently $$\mathbf{V}_{in} = \frac{100}{(200+j200)}\cdot 50 \text{ V}$$

$$\therefore \mathbf{V}_L = \frac{-100\times 50}{(200+j200)}$$

the negative sign being due to the phase change of π rad

$$\therefore \mathbf{I}_L = \frac{\mathbf{V}_L}{100} = \frac{-50}{200(1+j)}$$

$$= \tfrac{1}{8}(-1+j) \text{ A}$$

The magnitude of the load current

$$= |\mathbf{I}_L| = I_L = \frac{\sqrt{2}}{8} = 0{\cdot}178 \text{ A} \quad \textit{Ans.}$$

6. An inductor and a capacitor, each of reactance X, and two resistors of resistance R are connected to the terminals A, B, C of a balanced 3-phase supply as shown in Fig. 5.11. A high impedance voltmeter D is connected between the points a and c. The line voltages are $V_{AB} = V$, $V_{BC} = h^2V$, and $V_{CA} = hV$, where $h = \frac{1}{2}(-1+j\sqrt{3})$. Find the ratio X/R for which the voltmeter reads zero, and determine for this ratio the voltage applied to the voltmeter if the phase sequence of the supply is reversed.

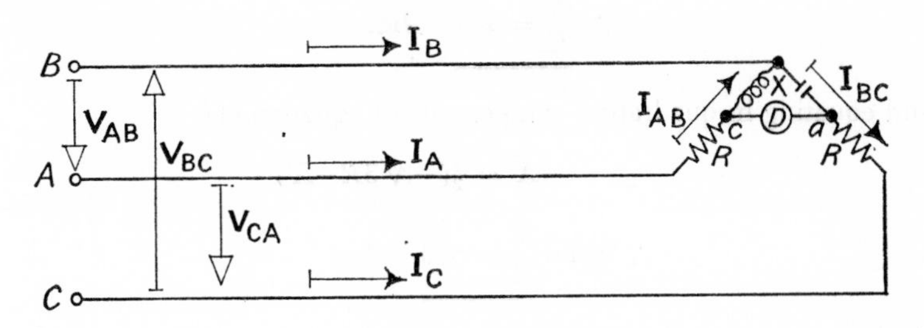

Fig. 5.11

Solution 1. Use the conventional directions of voltage and current as indicated in the figure above. (These were not given in the original question.)

2. Use the voltage $\mathbf{V_{AB}}$ as the reference vector, i.e. $\mathbf{V_{AB}} = V(1+j0)$.

3. In the first case the phase sequence is ABC.

By inspection of the circuit,

$$\mathbf{I_{AB}} = \frac{\mathbf{V_{AB}}}{R+jX} = \frac{V(1+j0)}{R+jX}$$

$$\mathbf{I_{BC}} = \frac{\mathbf{V_{BC}}}{R-jX} = \frac{h^2V}{R-jX}$$

Now the voltage drop

$$cB = \mathbf{I_{AB}}(jX) = \frac{jVX}{R+jX}$$

and the voltage drop

$$Ba = \mathbf{I_{BC}}(-jX) = \frac{-jh^2VX}{R-jX}$$

$\therefore$ The total voltage c to a

$$= \frac{jVX}{R+jX} + \frac{-jh^2VX}{R-jX} = 0$$

$$\therefore\ R-jX = h^2(R+jX)$$
$$= \tfrac{1}{2}(-1-j\sqrt{3})(R+jX)$$
$$= \tfrac{1}{2}[(-R+\sqrt{3}X)+j(-\sqrt{3}R-X)] \qquad (1)$$

$\therefore$ equating in phase components of equation (1),

$$R = \tfrac{1}{2}(-R+\sqrt{3}X)$$
$$\therefore\ \frac{X}{R} = \sqrt{3} \quad \textit{Ans.}$$

and equating in quadrature components of equation (1),

$$-X = \tfrac{1}{2}(-\sqrt{3}R-X)$$
$$\therefore\ \text{again}\ \frac{X}{R} = \sqrt{3} \quad \textit{Ans.}$$

With a reversal of phase sequence,

$$\mathbf{V}_{\mathbf{AB}} = V(1+j0) \quad \text{the reference vector}$$
$$\mathbf{V}_{\mathbf{BC}} = hV$$
$$\mathbf{V}_{\mathbf{CA}} = h^2\mathbf{V}$$

$\therefore$ Voltmeter reading = Voltage *ca*

$$= \mathbf{I}_{\mathbf{AB}}(jX)+\mathbf{I}_{\mathbf{BC}}(-jX)$$
$$= \frac{jVX}{R+jX}+\frac{-jhVX}{R-jX}$$
$$= \frac{jV\sqrt{3}}{1+j\sqrt{3}}-\frac{jVh\sqrt{3}}{1-j\sqrt{3}} \quad \text{since } X = \sqrt{3}R$$
$$= \frac{V}{4}[j\sqrt{3}(1-j\sqrt{3})-j\sqrt{3}.\tfrac{1}{2}(-1+j\sqrt{3})(1+j\sqrt{3})]$$
$$= \frac{V}{4}\cdot 3(1+j\sqrt{3})$$
$$= \frac{3V}{2} \text{ in magnitude} \quad \textit{Ans.}$$

$\therefore$ The voltmeter reads $3V/2$ with the phase sequence reversed, where V is the magnitude of the balanced line voltage.

PAPER NO. VI—JUNE, 1962

1. The bridge circuit shown in Fig. 6.1 is made up with two equal resistors r and two equal impedances $\mathbf{Z}$ as shown, such that $r = 2\ \Omega$, and $\mathbf{Z} = (1+j\sqrt{3})\ \Omega$. The bridge is supplied with unbalanced currents $\mathbf{I_R}$, $\mathbf{I_Y}$, and $\mathbf{I_B}$ from a 3-phase, 4-wire symmetrical supply, and the phase sequence is RYB. In the R line the positive, negative, and zero-sequence components of current are, respectively $(0+j50)$, $5(3+j\sqrt{3})$, and $(5+j0)$ amperes. Calculate the potential difference between the points P and Q of the bridge.

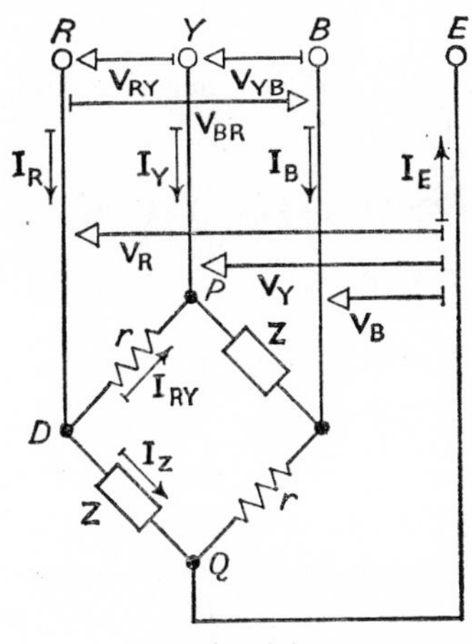

Fig. 6.1

Note: The conventional directions of voltage and current as shown in Fig. 6.1 were not given in the original question.

Solution

1. Use the conventional directions of voltage and current as shown in Fig. 6.1.

2. Choose the R phase voltage, i.e. $\mathbf{V_R}$ as the reference vector.

$$\therefore\ \mathbf{V_R} = V(1+j0);\ \mathbf{V_Y} = a^2V;\ \mathbf{V_B} = aV$$

3. The phase sequence was given as RYB.
By inspection of the figure evidently,

$$V_{PQ} = V_Y = V_B = V_R \quad \text{magnitudes}$$

since the supply voltages are symmetrical. Hence it is only necessary to find the magnitude of the symmetrical phase voltage.

Now by Kirchhoff's first law applied at the junction D,

$$\mathbf{I_R} = \mathbf{I_{RY}} + \mathbf{I_Z} = \frac{\mathbf{V_{RY}}}{r} + \frac{\mathbf{V_R}}{\mathbf{Z}}$$

$$= \frac{\mathbf{V_R}(1-a^2)}{2} + \frac{\mathbf{V_R}}{(1+j\sqrt{3})}$$

$$= V[\tfrac{1}{4}(3+j\sqrt{3}) + \tfrac{1}{4}(1-j\sqrt{3})] \quad \text{since } a^2 = -\tfrac{1}{2} - j\frac{\sqrt{3}}{2}$$

$$= V \tag{1}$$

Now $$\mathbf{I_R} = \mathbf{I_1} + \mathbf{I_2} + \mathbf{I_0}$$

where $\mathbf{I_1}$, $\mathbf{I_2}$, and $\mathbf{I_0}$ are the positive, negative, and zero-sequence components of current respectively.

$$\therefore \mathbf{I_R} = (0+j50) + 5(3+j\sqrt{3}) + (5+j0)$$

$$= 20 + j5(10+\sqrt{3})$$

$$\therefore V = |\mathbf{I_R}| = \sqrt{20^2 + 25(10+\sqrt{3})^2} = 62 \text{ V}$$

$$\therefore \text{Voltage } P \text{ to } Q = V_{PQ} = V = \underline{62 \text{ V}} \quad \textit{Ans.}$$

Note: The symmetrical line voltage is $62\sqrt{3} = 108$ V, which makes the question comparable with the American 3-phase, 110 V system.

2. Draw a block diagram for an error-actuated automatic control system for the position control of a rotatable mass, the system being stabilized by output-velocity feedback. Describe briefly the purpose of the essential elements and deduce the differential equation of the system neglecting friction.

A flywheel driven by an electric motor is automatically controlled to follow the movement of a handwheel. The inclusive moment of inertia of the flywheel is 100 kg-m^2 and the motor torque applied to it is 2500 Nm per radian of misalignment between the flywheel and the handwheel. A flywheel velocity of 1 rad/s produces a feedback torque on the flywheel of 600 Nm. The handwheel is suddenly turned through 90° when the system is at rest. Derive an expression for the subsequent angular position of the flywheel in relation to time and sketch the form of the function.

Solution

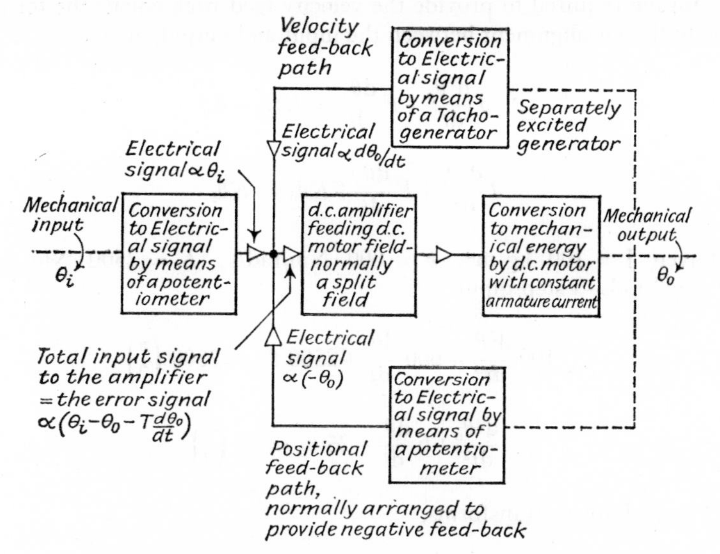

Fig. 6.2.—Block diagram of an error-actuated servo-merchanism employing velocity feed-back stabilization

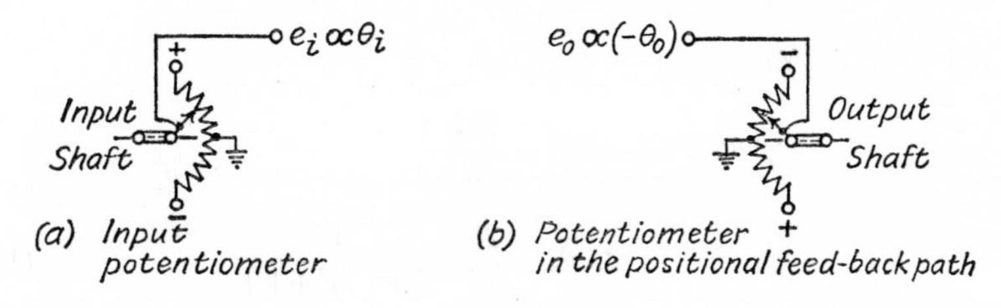

Fig. 6.3

The essential elements of the system should be evident from the diagrams. Let

θ_i = the input position in radians relative to some arbitrary reference,

θ_o = the output position in radians relative to some arbitrary reference,

J = the moment of inertia of the output shaft including all the moving parts in kg-m^2,

K = the torque in Nm per radian of misalignment between the output and input shafts,

F = the velocity feed-back constant in Nm/rad/s.

Now the total torque due to the acceleration of the output shaft plus the torque required to provide the velocity feed-back equals the torque due to the misalignment between the input and output shafts.

$$\therefore\ J\frac{d^2\theta_o}{dt^2}+F\frac{d\theta_o}{dt} = K(\theta_i-\theta_o)$$

or

$$J\frac{d^2\theta_o}{dt^2}+F\frac{d\theta_o}{dt}+K\theta_o = K\theta_i$$

Given J = 100 kg-m²; F = 600 Nm/rad/s; K = 2500 Nm/rad; $\theta_i = \pi/2$ rad—a step input.

$$\therefore\ 100\frac{d^2\theta_o}{dt^2}+600\frac{d\theta_o}{dt}+2500\,\theta_o = 2500\left(\frac{\pi}{2}\right)$$

$$\therefore\ \frac{d^2\theta_o}{dt^2}+6\frac{d\theta_o}{dt}+25\,\theta_o = 25\left(\frac{\pi}{2}\right)$$

Taking Laplace transforms,

$$s^2\bar{\theta}_o-s\theta_o(0)-\theta_o'(0)+6s\bar{\theta}_o-6\theta_o(0)+25\bar{\theta}_o = 25\left(\frac{\pi}{2s}\right)$$

when $t = 0$, $\theta_o = 0$ $\qquad\therefore\ \theta_o(0) = 0$

and $d\theta_o/dt = 0$ $\qquad\therefore\ \theta_o'(0) = 0$

$$\therefore\ \bar{\theta}_o(s^2+6s+25) = \frac{25\pi}{2}\cdot\frac{1}{s}$$

$$\therefore\ \bar{\theta}_o = \frac{25\pi}{2}\cdot\frac{1}{s[(s+3)^2+4^2]} \qquad (1)$$

Consider

$$\mathscr{L}^{-1}\frac{1}{(s-3)(s^2+4^2)} = \frac{1}{25}\mathscr{L}^{-1}\frac{9+16}{(s-3)(s^2+4^2)} \qquad (2)$$

$$= \frac{1}{25}(\varepsilon^{3t}-\tfrac{3}{4}\sin 4t-\cos 4t)$$

Wherever s occurs put $(s+3)$ in equation (2), which gives equation (1). Hence, by means of the shifting theorem,

$$\theta_o = \frac{25\pi}{2}\cdot\frac{1}{25}\cdot\varepsilon^{-3t}(\varepsilon^{3t}-\tfrac{3}{4}\sin 4t-\cos 4t)$$

$$= \frac{\pi}{2}\,[1-\varepsilon^{-3t}(\tfrac{3}{4}\sin 4t+\cos 4t)]$$

$$= \frac{\pi}{2}\,[1-\varepsilon^{-3t}.\tfrac{5}{4}\sin (4t+\alpha)] \quad \text{where } \alpha = \tan^{-1}\tfrac{4}{3} \quad \textit{Ans.}$$

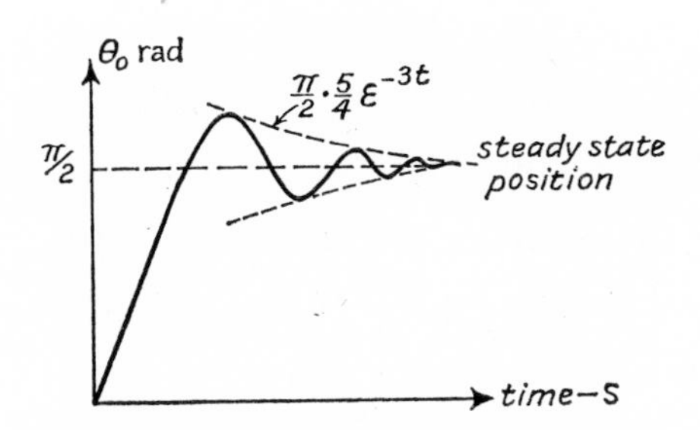

Fig. 6.4.—Sketch of the form of the output position with respect to time

3. A 4-terminal resistive network has input terminals A and B and output terminals C and D. The resistances measured across AB when terminals CD are first short-circuited and then open-circuited are, respectively, 720 Ω and 1240 Ω. The resistance measured across CD with AB open-circuited is 910 Ω. Determine the equivalent T-network and the image impedances. Hence calculate the insertion loss produced by the network when inserted between its image impedances.

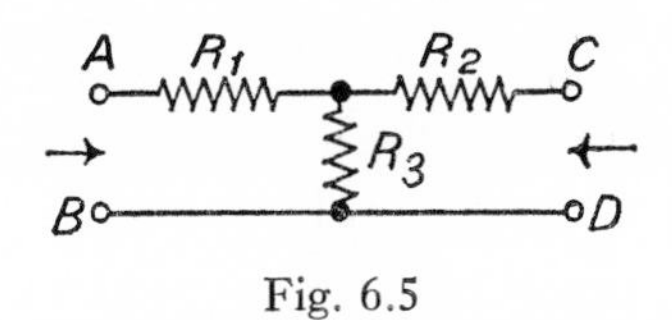

Fig. 6.5

Solution Now R_{AB} with CD on open-circuit

$$= 1240\ \Omega = R_1+R_3 \tag{1}$$

and R_{AB} with CD on short-circuit

$$= 720\ \Omega = R_1+\frac{R_2R_3}{R_2+R_3} \tag{2}$$

and R_{CD} with AB on open-circuit

$$= 910\ \Omega = R_2+R_3 \tag{3}$$

∴ Substituting equation (3) in equation (2),

$$720\times 910 = 910R_1+R_2R_3 \tag{4}$$

Substituting for R_1, from equation (1) in equation (4),

$$720\times 910 = 910(1240-R_3)+R_2R_3$$
$$= 910\times 1240+R_3(R_2-910)$$
$$= 910\times 1240+(910-R_2)(R_2-910)$$

$$\therefore\ (R_2-910)^2 = 910\times 520$$

$$\therefore\ R_2 = 910\pm\sqrt{910\times 520} = 910\pm 260\sqrt{7}\ \Omega$$

By inspection of equation (3) $R_2 < 910\ \Omega$ if R_3 is to be positive.

$$\therefore\ R_2 = 910-260\sqrt{7} = 222\ \Omega$$

and $R_3 = 910-222 = 688\ \Omega$ From equation (3)

and $R_1 = 1240-688 = 552\ \Omega$ from equation (1)

By the definition of image impedance:

$$R_{AB} = \sqrt{R_{OC-CD}.R_{SC-CD}}$$
$$= \sqrt{1240\times 720}$$
$$= 945\ \Omega$$

= the resistance looking into the terminals AB when CD is terminated by 695 Ω

Also $R_{CD} = \sqrt{R_{OC-AB}.R_{SC-AB}}$

$$= \sqrt{910\left(222+\frac{552\times 688}{552+688}\right)}$$

$$= 695\ \Omega$$

= the resistance looking into the terminals CD when AB is terminated by 945 Ω

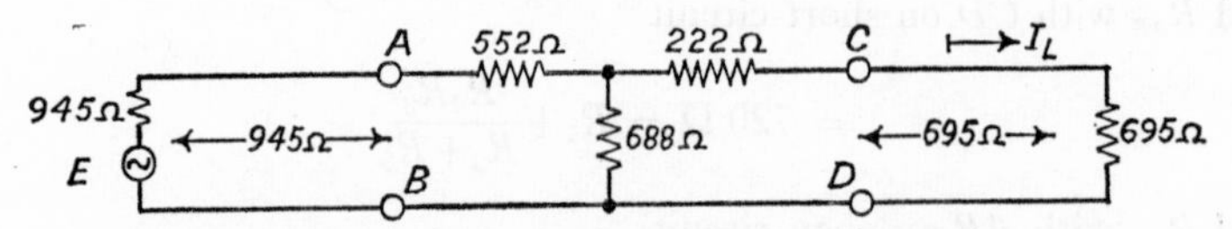

Fig. 6.6—Network inserted between its image impedances with generator E volts

With the 4-terminal network removed the load current

$$I_L' = \frac{E}{945+695} = \frac{E}{1640}\ \text{A}$$

In order to find the load current I_L, use Thévenin's theorem.

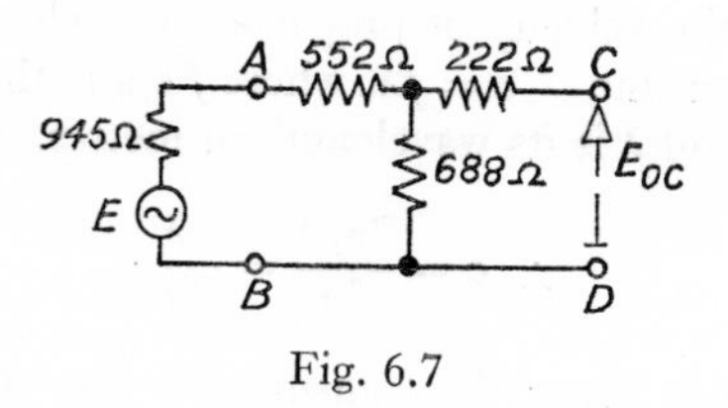

Fig. 6.7

With the load removed:

$$E_{OC} = \frac{E \times 688}{945+552+688}$$

$$= \frac{E \times 688}{2185}\ \text{V}$$

Now the 'looking in' resistance at the terminals CD, with the generator replaced by an impedance equal to its internal impedance $= 695\ \Omega$, by definition of image impedance.

$$\therefore\ I_L = \frac{E \times 688}{2185} \times \frac{1}{695+695} = \frac{E \times 688}{2185 \times 1390}\ \text{A}$$

$$\therefore\ \text{insertion loss} = 20 \log \frac{I_L'}{I_L}$$

$$= 20 \log \frac{E}{1640} \times \frac{2185 \times 1390}{E \times 688}$$

$$= 20 \log 2{\cdot}7$$

$$= 8{\cdot}63\ \text{db} \quad \textit{Ans.}$$

Note: If the generator E were replaced at the other end of the network, i.e. between terminals C and D, the magnitude of the load current in the image impedance of 945 Ω would be unchanged from that already found (the Reciprocity theorem). Hence the insertion loss would remain at 8·63 db.

4. Explain why the velocity of propagation of electromagnetic waves along a transmission line is normally less than that in free space.

A transmission line has a resistance of 15 Ω, negligible leakage, a capacitance of 0·02 μF, and an inductance of 5·0 mH, all per loop-mile. Calculate for a frequency of 796 c/s (*a*) the attenuation and phase-change coefficients and (*b*) the velocity of propagation.

Solution Now the velocity of propagation of electromagnetic waves along a transmission line $= c = f\lambda$, where f c/s is the frequency of the propagated wave, and λ is its wavelength in metres.

$$\therefore\ c = \frac{2\pi f\lambda}{2\pi} = \frac{\omega\lambda}{2\pi}$$

but λ is the distance along the transmission line such that the phase change is 2π rad.

$$\therefore\ \lambda = \frac{2\pi}{\beta}$$

and
$$c = \frac{\omega}{2\pi}\cdot\frac{2\pi}{\beta} = \frac{\omega}{\beta}$$

Now for a transmission line it may be shown that $\beta = \omega\sqrt{LC}$ rad

$$\therefore\ c = \frac{1}{\sqrt{LC}}\ \text{m/s} \tag{1}$$

Now for a twin-wire line

$$L = \frac{2\mu}{2\pi}\cdot\ln\frac{D}{r}\ \text{H/m}$$

$$C = \frac{2\pi\epsilon}{2\ln\dfrac{D}{r}}\ \text{F/m}$$

where D is the spacing between conductors and r is the radius.

and for a co-axial type line

$$L = \frac{\mu}{2\pi}\cdot\ln\frac{r_2}{r_1}\ \text{H/m}$$

$$C = \frac{2\pi\epsilon}{\ln\dfrac{r_2}{r_1}}\ \text{F/m}$$

where r_2 and r_1 are the outer and inner radii respectively.

Now substituting in equation (1), L and C for either twin-wire or co-axial line, gives

$$c = \frac{1}{\sqrt{\mu\epsilon}}$$

$$= \frac{1}{\sqrt{\mu_0\epsilon_0}} \cdot \frac{1}{\sqrt{\mu_r\epsilon_r}}$$

where μ_0, μ_r are the absolute and relative values of permeability respectively, and ϵ_0, ϵ_r are the absolute and relative values of permittivity respectively.

Now $$\frac{1}{\sqrt{\mu_0\epsilon_0}} = \frac{1}{\sqrt{4\pi\times 10^{-7}\times\frac{1}{36\pi}\times 10^{-9}}} = 3\times 10^8 \text{ m/s}$$

= the velocity of propagation of electro-magnetic waves in free space

$$\therefore\ c = \frac{3\times 10^8}{\sqrt{\mu_r\epsilon_r}} = \text{the phase velocity}$$

This equation shows that the presence of any material medium lowers the phase velocity. In free space $\mu_r = \epsilon_r = 1{\cdot}0$, and the velocity becomes the velocity of light, or the velocity of electromagnetic waves in free space.

For a twin-wire air-spaced transmission line, the velocity of propagation approaches the free-space velocity, but with co-axial type transmission lines the phase velocity is proportional to $1/\sqrt{\epsilon_r}$, and in practice the relative permittivity of the dielectric material will account for most of the reduction in velocity as compared with the free-space velocity.

Note: This is not the only possible solution to this question, which does not specify the type of transmission line. With a question of this nature the object is obviously to find out how much the student knows, and a solution other than that quoted may have been acceptable to the examiners.

Numerical portion

The propagation constant of the transmission line

$$= \gamma = \sqrt{(R+j\omega L)(G+j\omega C)}$$

where $R = 15\,\Omega$; $L = 5.10^{-3}$ H; $C = 0{\cdot}02.10^{-6}$ F; $G = 0$; $\omega = 2\pi \times 796 = 5.10^3$ rad/s

$$= \sqrt{(15+j5.10^3\times 5.10^{-3})(0+j5.10^3\times 0{\cdot}02.10^{-6})}$$

$$= 10^{-2}\sqrt{-25+j15} = 10^{-2}\sqrt{5}\,\sqrt{5{\cdot}83}\underline{/[\tan^{-1}(-\tfrac{3}{5})]/2}$$

$$= 0{\cdot}054\underline{/74^\circ{\cdot}31'}$$

$$= 0{\cdot}0144+j0{\cdot}052 = \alpha+j\beta$$

∴ The attenuation coefficient

$$= \alpha = 0{\cdot}0144 \text{ neper/mile}$$

$$= 0{\cdot}0144\times 8{\cdot}68 \text{ db/mile}$$

$$= \underline{0{\cdot}125 \text{ db/mile}} \quad \textit{Ans. (a)}$$

The phase change coefficient

$$= \beta = \underline{0{\cdot}052 \text{ rad/mile}} \quad \textit{Ans. (a)}$$

The velocity of propagation

$$= \frac{\omega}{\beta} = \frac{5000}{0{\cdot}052} = \underline{96{,}200 \text{ miles/s}} \quad \textit{Ans. (b)}$$

5. Discuss the difficulties that arise in calculations on circuits containing elements which have non-linear current/voltage characteristics.

A 12 Ω resistor is connected in series with a resistor for which the current/voltage relation is:

$$i = (5\times 10^{-2})v+(4\times 10^{-4})v^2+(1{\cdot}5\times 10^{-6})v^3$$

where i is amperes and v is in volts.

If a sinusoidal voltage of 100 V r.m.s. is applied to the combination, determine the two peak values of the current. Indicate a procedure by which the current waveform may be obtained.

Solution The difficulties that arise in calculations on circuits containing elements which have non-linear current/voltage characteristics may be illustrated by means of the example given in the question.

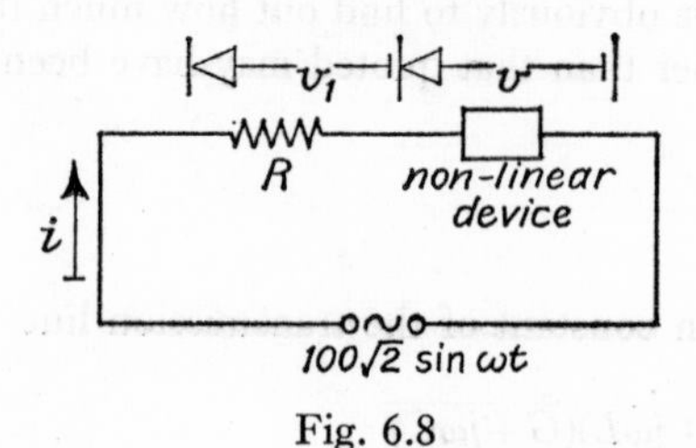

Fig. 6.8

Now evidently the total applied voltage

$$= 100\sqrt{2}\sin\omega t = v + v_1$$

$$\therefore\ v = 100\sqrt{2}.\sin\omega t - 12i$$

Thus, substituting in the given non-linear equation,

$$\begin{aligned} i = {} & (5\times10^{-2})(100\sqrt{2}.\sin\omega t - 12i) \\ & +(4\times10^{-4})(100\sqrt{2}.\sin\omega t - 12i)^2 \\ & +(1{\cdot}5\times10^{-6})(100\sqrt{2}.\sin\omega t - 12i)^3 \end{aligned} \qquad (1)$$

If equation (1) is expanded on the right-hand side the result will contain such items as the products of $i\sin\omega t$, $i^2\sin\omega t$, $i^2\sin^2\omega t, \ldots$ In order to solve this equation for i in terms of t, considerable mathematical manipulation would be required. The resultant equation is a cubic in i and $\sin\omega t$ which cannot be solved in general terms.

In this case in order to find the maximum values of i, it would be necessary to find $di/d(\omega t)$, which would involve one in a complex differential equation. If we assume, since no phase is involved, that the maximum values of the current occurs when the applied voltage is a maximum, then $\sin\omega t = 1$. This may be substituted in equation (1), but in order to solve for i it is necessary to solve a cubic equation, which could be achieved by the aid of Newton's approximations. (The author has checked the solution to this problem by solving the cubic equations involved on a digital computer.) With the involvement of the cumbersome mathematical methods, the obvious solution would appear to be readily achieved by graphical means.

Note: an alternative approach to this question might be based upon the non-linear equation obtained by means of Taylor's Theorem. It would be a useful exercise for the student to discuss alternative difficulties that arise in calculations on circuits which have non-linear current/voltage characteristics.

Graphical method

Plot the graph of the non-linear characteristic

$$i = (5.10^{-2})v + (4.10^{-4})v^2 + (1{\cdot}5.10^{-6})v^3$$

and also the linear characteristic given by $v_1 = 12i$. By adding the ordinates the overall characteristic is found. By projection of the peak values of the applied voltage of $\pm 100\sqrt{2}$ V, the corresponding values of the peak current may be found. From the graph, the peak values of the current were found to be 6·0 A and 2·6 A. *Ans.*

By choosing a suitable scale for ωt, the input voltage waveform may be projected on to the overall characteristic, and the resulting current waveform found. This is evident from the graph. *Ans.*

In order to plot the non-linear characteristic the following figures were calculated:

v volts	0	10	20	30	40	50	60	70	80
i amperes	0	0·54	1·17	1·90	2·74	3·69	4·76	5·97	7·33
v volts	−10	−20	−30	−40	−50	−60	−80	−100	−120
i amperes	−0·46	−0·96	−1·18	−1·46	−1·69	−1·88	−2·21	−2·50	−2·80

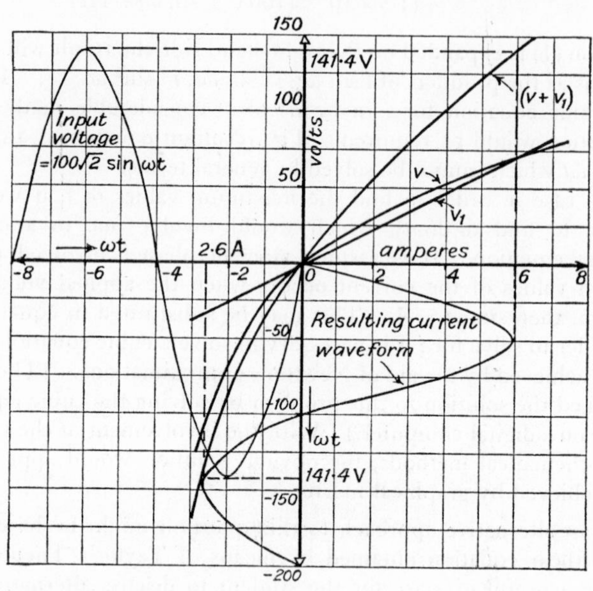

Fig. 6.9

6. Explain the terms travelling wave and standing wave as applied to transmission lines.

Two long transmission lines each having a surge impedance of 400 Ω are connected by a cable having a surge impedance of 50 Ω. If a short pulse of magnitude 10 kV travels along the first line towards the junction, determine from first principles the magnitude of the first and second pulses entering the line. State any assumptions made.

Solution *Travelling wave* is that waveform of voltage or current which is transmitted from the sending end of a transmission line towards the receiving end, or being reflected from the receiving end towards the sending end.

Standing wave is a result of the vector addition of a transmitted wave and the wave reflected from the termination in a transmission line. This gives rise to a stationary wave pattern along the line normally called the standing wave pattern.

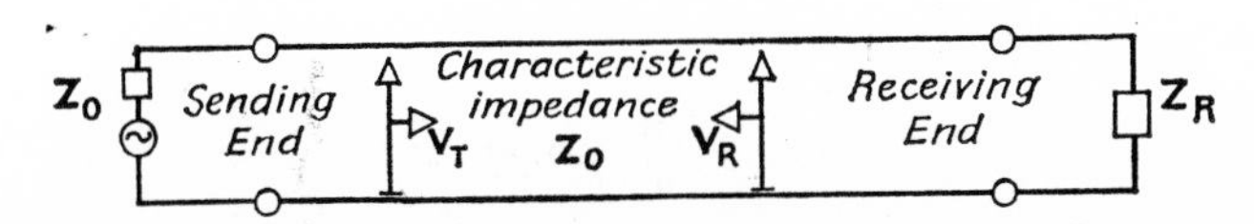

Fig. 6.10.—Transmission line terminated in an impedance $\mathbf{Z_R}$ not equal to the characteristic impedance $\mathbf{Z_0}$ of the line

$\mathbf{V_T}$ = wave travelling from the sending end to the receiving end,

$\mathbf{V_R}$ = wave travelling from the receiving end to the sending end,

$\mathbf{V_T}+\mathbf{V_R}$ = the standing wave voltage at a particular point along the line.

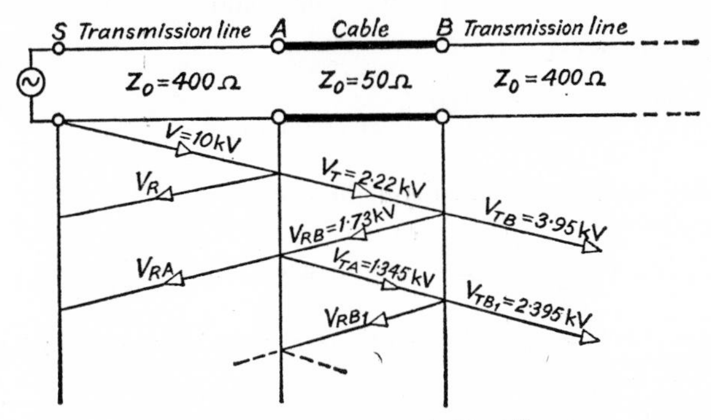

Fig. 6.11.—The Bewley lattice diagram

Now the voltage in the transmission line at the junction A
= the voltage in the cable at the junction B

$$\therefore\ V+V_R = V_T$$

$$\therefore\ 10+V_R = V_T \tag{1}$$

Also applying Kirchhoff's first law at the junction A,

$$I = I_R+I_T \tag{2}$$

Also

$$\frac{V}{I} = Z_0 = 400\ \Omega;\quad \frac{V_R}{I_R} = Z_0 = 400\ \Omega;\quad \frac{V_T}{I_T} = Z_0 = 50\ \Omega$$

$\therefore$ from equation (2),

$$\frac{10}{400} = \frac{V_R}{400} + \frac{V_T}{50}$$

$$\therefore\ 10 - V_R = 8V_T \tag{3}$$

Adding equations (1) and (3),

$$V_T = \frac{20}{9} = 2{\cdot}22 \text{ kV}$$

V_T now becomes the incident voltage in the cable towards the junction B.

$\therefore$ Similarly at the junction B,

$$\frac{20}{9} + V_{RB} = V_{TB} \tag{4}$$

and

$$\frac{20}{9 \times 50} = \frac{V_{RB}}{50} + \frac{V_{TB}}{400} \tag{5}$$

From equation (5),

$$\frac{160}{9} = 8V_{RB} + V_{TB} \tag{6}$$

Subtracting equation (4) from equation (6),

$$\therefore\ V_{RB} = \frac{140}{81} \text{ kV} \quad \text{and, hence,} \quad V_{TB} = \frac{320}{81} \text{ kV}$$

V_{RB} now becomes the incident voltage in the cable towards the junction A.

$\therefore$ Similarly, at the junction A,

$$\frac{140}{81} + V_{TA} = V_{RA} \tag{7}$$

and

$$\frac{140}{81 \times 50} = \frac{V_{TA}}{50} + \frac{V_{RA}}{400} \tag{8}$$

From equation (8),

$$\frac{140 \times 8}{81} = 8V_{TA} + V_{RA} \tag{9}$$

Subtracting equation (7) from equation (9),

$$\therefore\ V_{TA} = \frac{140 \times 7}{81 \times 9} = 1{\cdot}345 \text{ kV}$$

V_{TA} now becomes the incident voltage in the cable towards the junction B.

∴ Similarly, at the junction B,

$$1{\cdot}345 + V_{RB1} = V_{TB1} \tag{10}$$

and

$$\frac{1{\cdot}345}{50} = \frac{V_{TB1}}{400} + \frac{V_{RB1}}{50} \tag{11}$$

From equation (11)

$$8 \times 1{\cdot}345 = V_{TB1} + 8V_{RB1}$$

From equation (10)

$$8 \times 1{\cdot}345 = 8V_{TB1} - 8V_{RB1}$$

Adding

$$V_{TB1} = \frac{16 \times 1{\cdot}345}{9} = 2{\cdot}39 \text{ kV}$$

Hence the first two pulses entering the transmission line are of amplitude 3·95 kV and 2·39 kV respectively. *Ans.*

The following assumptions are made:

1. The line and the cable are loss-free; hence, at any point along either of them V/I is purely resistive and equal to Z_0.

2. The generator which supplies the initial 10 kV pulse is matched to the line system, thus there are no reflections from the sending end of the system.

3. The transmission line from B onwards is infinitely long, or it is correctly terminated, thus there are no reflections from the transmission line towards the junction B.

PAPER NO. VII—NOVEMBER, 1962

1. A coil having resistance and inductance carries a known periodic non-sinusoidal current. Derive an expression for the factor by which the impedance (referred to the fundamental frequency) is apparently increased when its value is taken as the quotient of the r.m.s. voltage and the r.m.s. current. Assume the current to contain a fundamental and a third-harmonic component.

Determine the percentage error in measuring the impedance of a coil in this way when the current contains a 20% fifth harmonic and a 10% seventh harmonic in addition to the fundamental. The coil has a reactance/resistance ratio of 4/1 at the fundamental frequency.

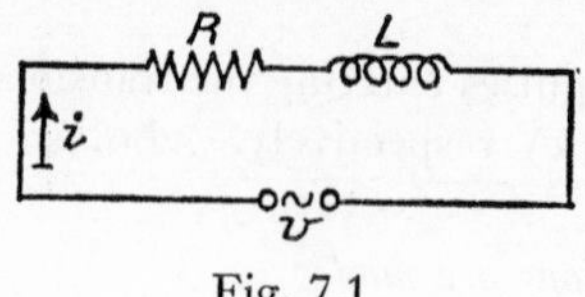

Fig. 7.1

Solution Let the instantaneous value of the steady state voltage applied to the circuit be given by:

$$v = V_1 \sin \omega t + V_3 \sin 3\omega t \qquad (1)$$

$$\therefore\ i = I_1 \sin(\omega t - \phi_1) + I_3 \sin(3\omega t - \phi_3) \qquad (2)$$

where $\phi_1 = \tan^{-1} \omega L/R$ and $\phi_3 = \tan^{-1} 3\omega L/R$

Now the r.m.s. value of the applied voltage

$$= V = \sqrt{\tfrac{1}{2}(V_1^2 + V_3^2)} \qquad (3)$$

and the r.m.s. value of the current flowing

$$= I = \sqrt{\tfrac{1}{2}(I_1^2 + I_3^2)} \qquad (4)$$

The magnitude of the circuit impedance at the fundamental frequency

$$= Z_1 = \frac{V_1}{I_1} = \sqrt{R^2 + (\omega L)^2}\ \Omega \qquad (5)$$

The magnitude of the circuit impedance at the third harmonic frequency

$$= Z_3 = \frac{V_3}{I_3} = \sqrt{R^2 + (3\omega L)^2}\ \Omega \qquad (6)$$

The magnitude of the apparent circuit impedance

$$= Z = \frac{V}{I} = \frac{\sqrt{\frac{1}{2}(V_1^2+V_3^2)}}{\sqrt{\frac{1}{2}(I_1^2+I_3^2)}} = \sqrt{\frac{I_1^2(R^2+\omega^2L^2)+I_3^2(R^2+9\omega^2L^2)}{I_1^2+I_3^2}}\ \Omega \quad (7)$$

Hence, the impedance, when it is taken as the quotient of the r.m.s. voltage and the r.m.s. current, is apparently increased, as given by the expression:

$$\sqrt{\frac{I_1^2(R^2+\omega^2L^2)+I_3^2(R^2+9\omega^2L^2)}{I_1^2+I_3^2}} - \sqrt{R^2+\omega^2L^2}\ \Omega \quad (8)$$

Hence, it is evident that, when the current contains third, fifth, seventh harmonics, etc., the percentage increase in impedance, referred to the fundamental frequency, is given by the expression:

$$\frac{\sqrt{\dfrac{I_1^2(R^2+\omega^2L^2)+I_3^2(R^2+9\omega^2L^2)+I_5^2(R^2+25\omega^2L^2)+\cdots}{I_1^2+I_3^2+I_5^2+\cdots}} - \sqrt{R^2+\omega^2L^2}}{\sqrt{(R^2+\omega^2L^2)}} \times 100\% \quad \textit{Ans.}$$

Using the figures given in the question

$$I_3 = 0; \quad I_5 = \tfrac{1}{5}I_1; \quad I_7 = \tfrac{1}{100}I_1; \quad \omega L = 4R$$

∴ Substituting in the above equation, the percentage error in measuring a coil in this way

$$= \frac{\sqrt{\dfrac{I_1^2(R^2+16R^2)+(I_1^2/25)(R^2+400R^2)+(I_1^2/100)(R^2+784R^2)}{I_1^2+I_1^2/25+I_1^2/100}} - \sqrt{R^2+16R^2}}{\sqrt{R^2+16R^2)}} \times 100\%$$

$$= \left\{\sqrt{\frac{\dfrac{17+401/25+785/100}{1+1/25+1/100}}{17}} - 1\right\} \times 100\%$$

$\simeq$ 51% *Ans.*

Comments: The relatively high percentage of fifth and seventh harmonic content of the current has considerable effect upon the apparent impedance of the circuit, indicating the undesirability of such harmonics in practice.

2. The bridge shown in Fig. 7.2 is energized from a low-impedance source and has a high-impedance detector which is not phase sensitive. If the balanced conditions exist, derive an expression for the voltage sensitivity S of the detector with respect to a small change in the value of C. Show that, to a first approximation, S is directly proportional to frequency in the low frequency range and inversely proportional to frequency in the high frequency range of operation.

Assuming that the bridge arms are not altered, how might the sensitivity be made independent of frequency?

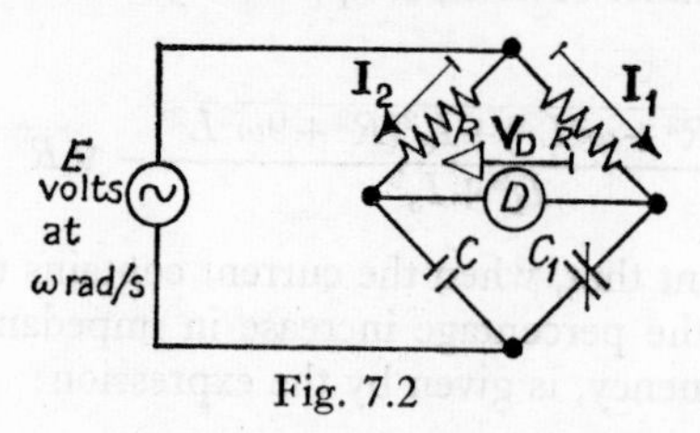

Fig. 7.2

Note: The conventional directions of voltage and current as indicated in the above figure were not given in the original question.

Solution Assuming a low impedance generator, and a high impedance detector, then by Kirchhoff's second law the detector voltage is evidently:

$$\mathbf{V_D} = \mathbf{I}_2R-\mathbf{I}_1R$$

$$= \frac{ER}{R+\dfrac{1}{j\omega C}}-\frac{ER}{R+\dfrac{1}{j\omega C_1}} \quad \text{with } E(1+j0) \text{ as the reference vector}$$

$$= E\cdot\frac{j\omega(RC-RC_1)}{(1+j\omega CR)(1+j\omega C_1R)} \tag{1}$$

For the detector voltage $\mathbf{V_D}$ to be zero volts, i.e. the bridge to be balanced, it is evident from equation (1) that $RC = RC_1$ or $C = C_1$. When C_1 changes by a small amount, then $\mathbf{V_D}$ also changes. Let $\mathrm{d}C_1$ = a small change in C_1 and the corresponding small change in $V_D = \mathrm{d}V_D$.

Now the magnitude of $\mathbf{V_D}$ is:

$$V_D = \frac{ER\omega(C-C_1)}{\sqrt{1+(\omega CR)^2}\,.\sqrt{1+(\omega C_1R)^2}}$$

$$\therefore\ \mathrm{d}V_D = \frac{ER\omega(C-C_1-\mathrm{d}C_1)}{\sqrt{1+(\omega CR)^2}\,.\sqrt{1+\{\omega R(C_1+\mathrm{d}C_1)^2\}}} \tag{2}$$

Now since the change in C_1 is small $C_1+\mathrm{d}C_1 \simeq C_1$. Also the bridge is still assumed to be balanced, $\therefore$ $C = C_1$. Hence, from equation (2),

$$\mathrm{d}V_D = \frac{ER\omega\,.\mathrm{d}C_1}{\sqrt{1+(\omega CR)^2}\,.\sqrt{1+(\omega C_1R)^2}}$$

The bridge sensitivity is therefore defined as

$$S = \frac{dV_D}{dC_1} = \frac{ER\omega}{\sqrt{1+(\omega CR)^2}.\sqrt{1+(\omega C_1R)^2}} \quad \textit{Ans.} \qquad (3)$$

At relatively low frequencies it is evident that

$$(\omega CR)^2 \ll 1 \quad \text{and also} \quad (\omega C_1R)^2 \ll 1$$

∴ From equation (3), the bridge sensitivity $S = \omega ER$ at low frequencies, i.e. *S is directly proportional to ω*, or *directly proportional to frequency*, since $\omega = 2\pi f$.

At high frequencies

$$(\omega CR)^2 \gg 1 \quad \text{and also} \quad (\omega C_1R)^2 \gg 1$$

∴ From equation (3), the bridge sensitivity $S = E/\omega RCC_1$ at high frequencies; i.e. *S is inversely proportional to ω*, or *inversely proportional to frequency*.

If in the original bridge the low impedance generator and the high impedance detector are interchanged, then by Kirchhoff's second law it is evident that

$$\mathbf{V_D} = E\left\{\frac{R}{2R} - \frac{\frac{1}{j\omega C}}{\frac{1}{j\omega C}+\frac{1}{j\omega C_1}}\right\}$$

$$= \frac{E(RC-RC_1)}{2R(C+C_1)}$$

∴ as in the first circuit arrangement, the condition for balance is $C = C_1$.

Now $$dV_D = \frac{E(RC-RC_1-R\,dC_1)}{2R(C+C_1+dC_1)}$$

$$\therefore S = \frac{dV_D}{dC_1} = \frac{E}{2(C+C_1)}$$

Hence, the bridge sensitivity S is made independent of frequency.

Note: Students often ask about the negative sign in the above expressions. This is accounted for by the fact that the bridge sensitivity is defined in terms of magnitude only.

3. A uniform transmission line is sometimes represented by lumped circuit elements. Discuss the limitations of such a representation.

For the purpose of calculating the phase-shift between input and output voltages a length of loss-free transmission line is represented by the T-section of Fig. 7.3. Calculate the error in the result at a frequency of $1/\pi\sqrt{(LC)}$ c/s. Both line and section are terminated in their respective characteristic impedances. The propagation coefficient of the section is given by

$$\cosh \gamma = 1 - \tfrac{1}{2}\omega^2 LC$$

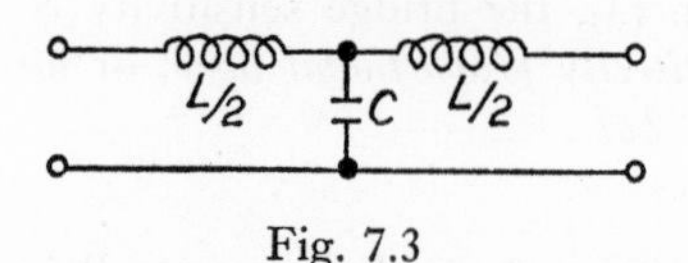

Fig. 7.3

Solution The following points discuss the limitations of representing a uniform transmission line, which has distributed primary constants, by lumped circuit elements. The accuracy of representation is a comparison between the measured or calculated values of the sending end voltage, current, and power factor of the lumped circuit element representation, and the measured values of the same parameters on the uniform transmission line, both systems having the same receiving end conditions.

1. The lumped circuit elements will only approximately represent the uniform transmission line at one particular frequency, or to an accepted degree of accuracy over a very limited narrow band of frequencies.

2. Depending upon the electrical length of the line, i.e. its physical length compared with its wavelength at the operating frequency, the lumped circuit representation will become less accurate as the electrical length increases. Electrically short lengths of line may be represented with considerable accuracy by means of nominal-T or nominal-π networks.

3. A transmission line may be used either at power frequencies or radio frequencies, in which case the physical construction of the lines would differ considerably. At radio frequencies the end to end capacity of the transmission line may be considerably different from that of the lumped circuit representation. This could lead to considerable inaccuracy in the representation of the transmission line.

4. With lumped circuit elements it is only possible to calculate or measure the sending end conditions, and it is not possible to observe the standing wave pattern of voltage or current which would normally be present along the uniform transmission line. It may be of practical importance with radio frequency transmission lines to be able to observe the standing wave pattern which could not be achieved from the lumped circuit elements.

5. The transmission line constants **A, B, C, D** enable the sending end conditions to be found, knowing the receiving end conditions by means of the equations $\mathbf{V_S} = \mathbf{AV_R}+\mathbf{BI_R}$ and $\mathbf{I_S} = \mathbf{CV_R}+\mathbf{DI_R}$. A comparison is given in Fig. 7.4 of the **A, B, C, D** constants for a uniform transmission line and the equivalent circuit containing lumped circuit elements.

Fig. 7.4. Comparison of **A, B, C, D** constants for a uniform transmission line with distributed constants and equivalent circuits containing lumped circuit elements

	A	B	C	D	Y	Z_0
Dimensions	Unity	Ohms	Mhos	Unity	Unity	Ohms
Line with distributed constants	$\cosh \gamma l$	$Z_0 \sinh \gamma l$	$\frac{1}{Z_0} \sinh \gamma l$	$\cosh \gamma l$	$\sqrt{\mathbf{y}.\mathbf{z}}$	$\sqrt{\frac{\mathbf{z}}{\mathbf{y}}}$
Using hyperbolic expansions	$1+\frac{\mathbf{YZ}}{2}$	$\mathbf{Z}\left(1+\frac{\mathbf{YZ}}{6}\right)$	$\mathbf{Y}\left(1+\frac{\mathbf{YZ}}{6}\right)$	$1+\frac{\mathbf{YZ}}{2}$	$\sqrt{\mathbf{y}.\mathbf{z}}$	$\sqrt{\frac{\mathbf{z}}{\mathbf{y}}}$
Short line with lumped constants $\mathbf{y} = 0$, $\mathbf{z} = r+jx$	1·0	$\mathbf{z}\mathrm{l} = R+jX = \mathbf{Z}$	0	1·0	0	∞
Nominal π, $\mathbf{y} = jb$, $\mathbf{z} = r+jx$	$1+\frac{\mathbf{YZ}}{2}$	$\mathbf{Z}$	$\mathbf{Y}\left(1+\frac{\mathbf{YZ}}{4}\right)$	$1+\frac{\mathbf{YZ}}{2}$	$\sqrt{(r+jx)jb}$	$\sqrt{\frac{r+jx}{jb}}$
Nominal T, $\mathbf{y} = jb$, $\mathbf{z} = r+jx$	$1+\frac{\mathbf{YZ}}{2}$	$\mathbf{Z}\left(1+\frac{\mathbf{YZ}}{4}\right)$	$\mathbf{Y}$	$1+\frac{\mathbf{YZ}}{2}$	$\sqrt{(r+jx)jb}$	$\sqrt{\frac{r+jx}{jb}}$

where r = resistance in ohms per unit length of uniform transmission line
x = inductive reactance per unit length of uniform transmission line
g = conductance in mhos per unit length
b = susceptance in mhos per unit length
$\mathbf{Z}$ = total series impedance = $(r+jx)\mathrm{l}$ ohms
$\mathbf{Y}$ = shunt resistance = $(g+jb)\mathrm{l}$ mhos

Numerical portion

Now $$\cosh \gamma = 1-\tfrac{1}{2}\omega^2 LC = 1-\frac{1}{2}\left(2\pi.\frac{1}{\pi\sqrt{LC}}\right)^2 LC = -1$$

$$\therefore\ \gamma = \cosh^{-1}(-1) = \ln \varepsilon^{j\pi} = j\pi$$

The propagation coefficient of the T-section

$$= \gamma = \alpha+j\beta = j\pi$$

$\therefore$ Equating in quadrature components gives the phase change coefficient $\beta = \pi$ rad.

Now for the transmission line

$$\gamma = \sqrt{(R+j\omega L)(G+j\omega C)}$$

If the line is loss-free, $R = 0$ and $G = 0$.

$$\therefore \gamma = j\omega\sqrt{LC} = \alpha + j\beta$$

$\therefore$ Equating in quadrature components gives the phase change coefficient

$$\beta = \omega\sqrt{LC} = 2\pi . \frac{1}{\pi\sqrt{LC}} . \sqrt{LC} = 2 \text{ rad}$$

Hence the error in the result of assuming the transmission line as represented by the T-section is $(\pi - 2)$ rad, too great. *Ans.*

4. An uncharged capacitor C having a leakage (shunt) resistance R is connected in series with a resistor R_1. A direct voltage V is suddenly applied to this circuit: derive an expression for the subsequent variation with time of the voltage across R_1. Sketch the time variation of the current in C and R_1.

If $V = 2$ kV, $C = 0{\cdot}5$ μF, $R_1 = 0{\cdot}1$ MΩ, and the steady voltage across R_1 is 200 V, determine the leakage resistance R of the capacitor.

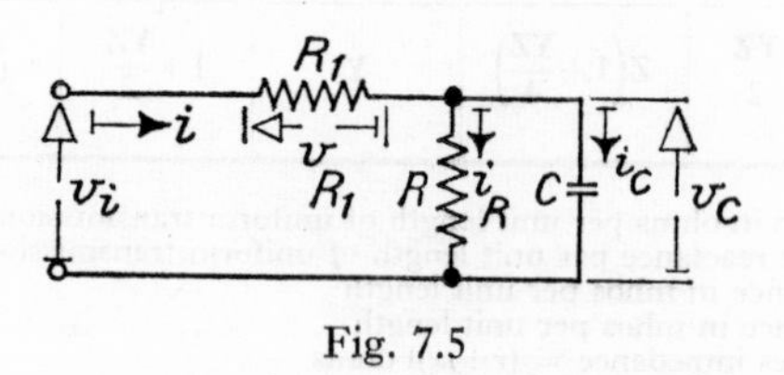

Fig. 7.5

Solution Since the capacitor C is uncharged, the initial energy conditions are zero. Let:

$$p = j\omega$$

By inspection of Fig. 7.5,

$$v_{R_1} = \frac{v_i R_1}{R_1 + \dfrac{R\left(\dfrac{1}{pC}\right)}{R + \dfrac{1}{pC}}}$$

$$= \frac{R_1\left(R+\frac{1}{pC}\right)}{R_1\left(R+\frac{1}{pC}\right)+R\frac{1}{pC}}\cdot v_i$$

$$= \frac{p+\frac{1}{RC}}{p+\frac{R+R_1}{RR_1C}}\cdot v_i$$

$$= \frac{p+\frac{1}{RC}}{p+\alpha}\cdot v_i \quad \text{where } \alpha = \frac{R+R_1}{RR_1C}$$

Now $v_i = V$, which is a step input. Hence, $\bar{v}_i = V/p$.

$\therefore$ Taking Laplace transforms,

$$\bar{v}_{R_1} = \frac{p+\frac{1}{RC}}{p+\alpha}\cdot\frac{V}{p}$$

$$= V\left[\frac{1}{p+\alpha}+\frac{1}{RC}\cdot\frac{1}{\alpha}\cdot\frac{\alpha}{p(p+\alpha)}\right]$$

$$= V\left[\frac{1}{p+\alpha}+\frac{R_1}{R+R_1}\cdot\frac{\alpha}{p(p+\alpha)}\right]$$

Hence, using the table of inverse Laplace transforms,

$$v_{R_1} = \mathbf{V}\left[\varepsilon^{-\alpha t}+\frac{R_1}{R+R_1}\left(1-\varepsilon^{-\alpha t}\right)\right]$$

$$= \frac{V}{R+R_1}\cdot\left(R_1+R\varepsilon^{-\alpha t}\right) \quad \text{where } \alpha = \frac{R+R_1}{RR_1C} \quad \textit{Ans.} \qquad (1)$$

Now $$v_c = v_i - v_{R_1} = V\left(1-\frac{R_1}{R+R_1}-\frac{R}{R+R_1}\cdot\varepsilon^{-\alpha t}\right)$$

$$= \frac{VR}{R+R_1}\cdot(1-\varepsilon^{-\alpha t})$$

$$\therefore q = Cv_c = \frac{VRC}{R+R_1}\cdot(1-\varepsilon^{-\alpha t})$$

= the instantaneous charge on the capacitor C

Now $$i_c = \frac{dq}{dt} = \frac{VRC}{R+R_1}\cdot\frac{R+R_1}{RR_1C}\cdot\varepsilon^{-\alpha t}$$

$$\therefore\ i_c = \frac{V}{R_1}\cdot\varepsilon^{-\alpha t}\ \text{A} \quad \textit{Ans.} \tag{2}$$

Also, from the equation for v_{R_1},

$$i = \frac{V}{R+R_1}\cdot\left(1+\frac{R}{R_1}\cdot\varepsilon^{-\alpha t}\right)\ \text{A} \quad \textit{Ans.} \tag{3}$$

By inspection of equation (1) the steady state voltage across R_1

$$= \frac{VR_1}{R+R_1} = 200 = \frac{2.10^3\times 0{\cdot}1.10^6}{R+0{\cdot}1.10^6}$$

$$\therefore\ 200(R+0{\cdot}1.10^6) = 200.10^6$$

$\therefore$ The leakage resistance $R = 0{\cdot}9\ \text{M}\Omega$ *Ans.*

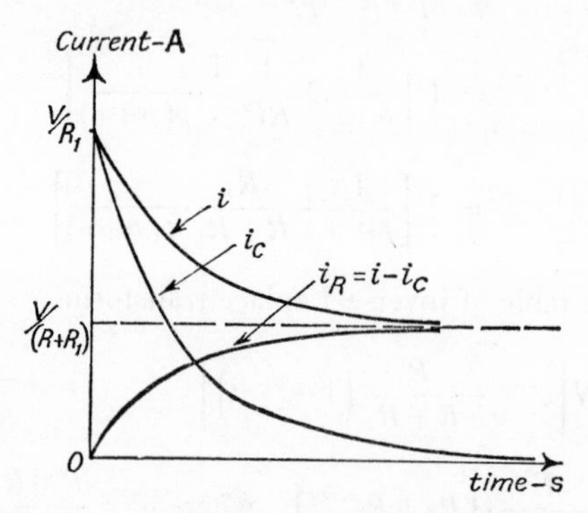

Fig. 7.6.—Sketch of the time variation of the currents in the circuit

5. An unbalanced star-connected load consists of a capacitor of reactance $X_A = -(j10\sqrt{3})\ \Omega$ and two resistors $R_B = 60\ \Omega$ and $R_C = 30\ \Omega$, as shown in Fig. 7.7. The power is measured by the two-wattmeter method with wattmeters W_1 and W_2. The load is connected to a symmetrical 3-phase supply ABC with line voltages $V_{AB} = 300$ V, $V_{BC} = h^2300$ V, and $V_{CA} = h300$ V, where $h = \frac{1}{2}(-1+j\sqrt{3})$. Calculate the readings of the two wattmeters W_1 and W_2 and the power in each arm of the load.

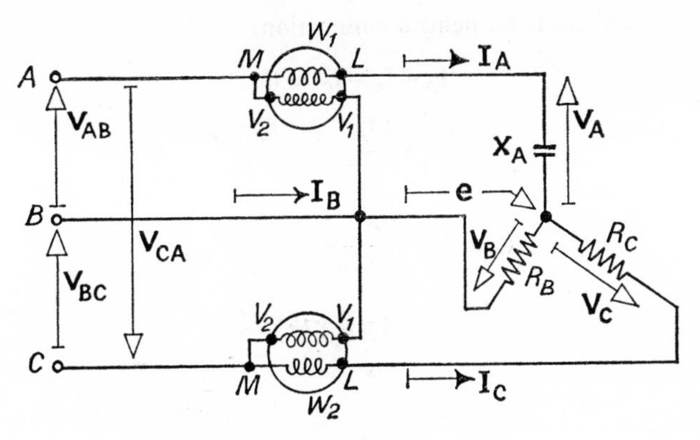

Fig. 7.7

Let **e** volt = the potential difference between the star-point of the load and the neutral point of the generator.

The conventional directions of voltage and current, and the wattmeter coils were not shown in the original question.

Note: with all problems in 3-phase circuitry it is necessary to quote the following facts. A problem worked out without these facts has no meaning, and the student will lose a considerable number of marks, especially if his arithmetic is incorrect.

Solution 1. Using the conventional directions of voltage and current as illustrated in Fig. 7.7.

2. Choose the generator A phase voltage as the reference vector, i.e.

$$\mathbf{E_A} = E(1+j0)$$

3. In this particular question the phase sequence is evidently ABC.

4. For the wattmeters assume that if the current in the current coil flows from M to L, and for the voltage coil if $V_2 > V_1$ then the wattmeter will read positive. (The symbols shown on the wattmeter were not given in the original question.)

Applying Kirchhoff's second law around each phase,

$$\mathbf{I_A} = \frac{\mathbf{V_A}}{\mathbf{X_A}} = \frac{\mathbf{E_A}-\mathbf{e}}{-j10\sqrt{3}} = \frac{E-\mathbf{e}}{-j10\sqrt{3}} \text{ A} \tag{1}$$

$$\mathbf{I_B} = \frac{\mathbf{V_B}}{R_B} = \frac{h^2\mathbf{E_A}-\mathbf{e}}{60} = \frac{h^2E-\mathbf{e}}{60} \text{ A} \tag{2}$$

$$\mathbf{I_C} = \frac{\mathbf{V_C}}{R_C} = \frac{h\mathbf{E_A}-\mathbf{e}}{30} = \frac{hE-\mathbf{e}}{30} \text{ A} \tag{3}$$

Also, since there is no neutral connection,

$$\mathbf{I_A}+\mathbf{I_B}+\mathbf{I_C} = 0$$

$$\therefore \frac{E-\mathbf{e}}{-j10\sqrt{3}}+\frac{h^2E-\mathbf{e}}{60}+\frac{hE-\mathbf{e}}{30} = 0$$

$$\therefore \mathbf{e} = \frac{E(h^2+2h+j2\sqrt{3})}{(3+j2\sqrt{3})}$$

$$= \frac{E}{2}\cdot\frac{(-3+j5\sqrt{3})}{(3+j2\sqrt{3})}$$

since $h^2 = \frac{1}{2}(-1-j\sqrt{3})$,
$h = \frac{1}{2}(-1+j\sqrt{3})$

$$= \frac{E}{2}\cdot(1+j\sqrt{3}) \quad \text{by rotationalization}$$

$$\therefore \mathbf{I_A} = \frac{E-\frac{E}{2}(1+j\sqrt{3})}{-j10\sqrt{3}}$$

$$= \frac{E}{2}\cdot\frac{(1-j\sqrt{3})}{(-j10\sqrt{3})}$$

$$= \frac{E}{20\sqrt{3}}\cdot(\sqrt{3}+j)$$

$$= \frac{300}{\sqrt{3}}\cdot\frac{1}{20\sqrt{3}}\cdot(\sqrt{3}+j)$$

$$= 5(\sqrt{3}+j)\text{ A} \tag{4}$$

And

$$\mathbf{I_C} = \frac{hE-\frac{E}{2}(1+j\sqrt{3})}{30}$$

$$= \frac{E}{60}(-2)$$

$$= \frac{300}{\sqrt{3}}\cdot\frac{(-2)}{60}$$

$$= -\frac{10}{\sqrt{3}}\text{ A} \tag{5}$$

With E as the reference vector

$$\mathbf{V_{AB}} = \mathbf{E_A} - \mathbf{E_B} = E(1-h^2)$$

Also

$$\mathbf{V_{BC}} = \mathbf{E_B} - \mathbf{E_C} = E(h^2-h)$$

Now wattmeter W_1 reads the dot product of $\mathbf{I_A} \times \mathbf{V_{AB}}$

$$= \text{dot product of } 5(\sqrt{3}+j)\frac{300}{\sqrt{3}}\cdot(1-h^2)$$

$$= \text{dot product of } \frac{1500}{\sqrt{3}}\cdot(\sqrt{3}+j)\left(\frac{3}{2}+j\frac{\sqrt{3}}{2}\right)$$

$$= \frac{1500}{\sqrt{3}}\left(\frac{3\sqrt{3}}{2}+\frac{\sqrt{3}}{2}\right) \quad \text{Note the sign}$$

$$= 3 \text{ kW}$$

Hence, W_1 reads 3 kW *Ans.*

Also wattmeter W_2 reads the dot product of $\mathbf{I_C} \times \mathbf{V_{CB}}$

$$= \text{dot product of } -\mathbf{I_C} \times \mathbf{V_{BC}}$$

$$= \text{dot product of } \frac{10}{\sqrt{3}}\cdot\frac{300}{\sqrt{3}}\cdot(h^2-h)$$

$$= \text{dot product of } \frac{10}{\sqrt{3}}\cdot\frac{300}{\sqrt{3}}\cdot(-j\sqrt{3})$$

$$= 0$$

Note: the wattmeter reads power which is a real quality.

Hence, wattmeter W_2 reads zero W *Ans.*

Since this is the two-wattmeter method of measuring power, then wattmeter W_1 reads the total power in the unbalanced load; also, since no power is dissipated in the capacitor, assumed to be loss-free, then evidently:

$$\text{the power in } R_B = 3\times\frac{60}{90} = 2 \text{ kW} \quad \textit{Ans.}$$

$$\text{the power in } R_C = 3\times\frac{30}{90} = 1 \text{ kW} \quad \textit{Ans.}$$

Aliter: From equation (5)

$$I_C = \frac{10}{\sqrt{3}} \text{ A}$$

$$\therefore \text{ Power in the resistor } R_C = I_C{}^2 R_C = \left(\frac{10}{\sqrt{3}}\right)^2 \times 30 = 1 \text{ kW}$$

Also from equation (2)

$$\mathbf{I_B} = \frac{h^2E - \dfrac{E}{2}\cdot(1+j\sqrt{3})}{60}$$

$$= \frac{E}{120}\cdot(2h^2-1-j\sqrt{3})$$

$$= \frac{E}{120}\cdot 2(-1-j\sqrt{3})$$

$$\therefore\ I_B = \frac{300}{\sqrt{3}}\cdot\frac{2}{120}\cdot 2 = \frac{10}{\sqrt{3}}\ \text{A}$$

$$\therefore\ \text{Power in the resistor } R_B = I_B{}^2.R_B = \left(\frac{10}{\sqrt{3}}\right)^2\times 60 = 2\ \text{kW}$$

Note: By inspection of the vector diagram shown in Fig. 7.8 it is evident that $\mathbf{I_C}$ is 180° out of phase with $\mathbf{E_A}$ and leading $\mathbf{V_{CB}}$ by 90°. Now the reading of wattmeter W_2 is proportional to $\mathbf{V_{CB}}\times$ the projection of $\mathbf{I_C}$ on to $\mathbf{V_{CB}}$, i.e. $\propto \cos 90°$ which is zero.

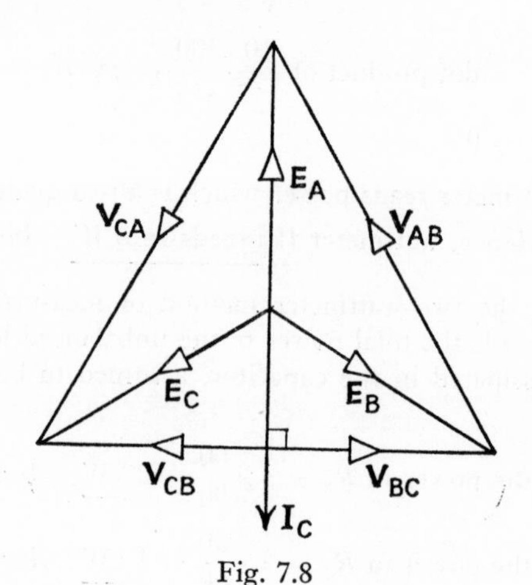

Fig. 7.8

6. Show analytically:

(*a*) how a simple *RC* circuit may be used to obtain an output voltage which is approximately the time integral of an input voltage; and

(*b*) how the performance of this integrator may be improved by using a suitable high-gain d.c. amplifier.

Hence, give in a diagram, with brief comments, the essential elements and connections for an electronic analogue computing system that could be used to solve an equation of the form

$$a\frac{d^2x}{dt^2}+b\frac{dx}{dt}+cx = 0$$

where a, b, and c are constants and x is a variable.

Solution

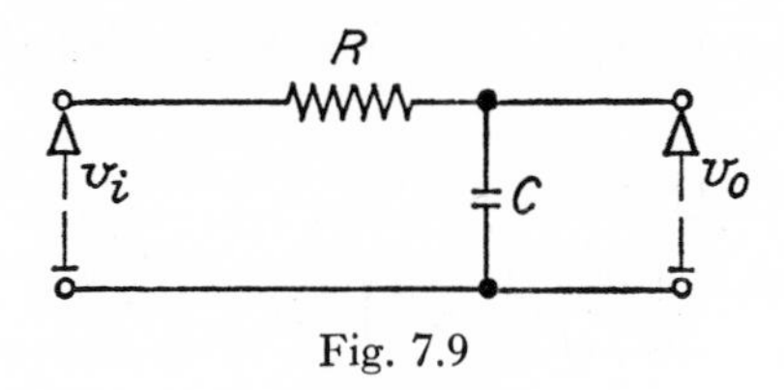

Fig. 7.9

The output voltage v_0 of the CR circuit

$$= \frac{v_i \dfrac{1}{pC}}{R+\dfrac{1}{pC}} = \frac{1}{CR}\cdot\frac{1}{p}\cdot v_i \quad \text{if } R \gg \frac{1}{pC}$$

where $p = j\omega$ and is also comparable with d/dt.

$$\therefore\ v_o = \frac{1}{CR}\int_0^t v_i\, dt \quad \textit{Ans.}$$

Hence the output voltage is approximately the time integral of the input voltage.

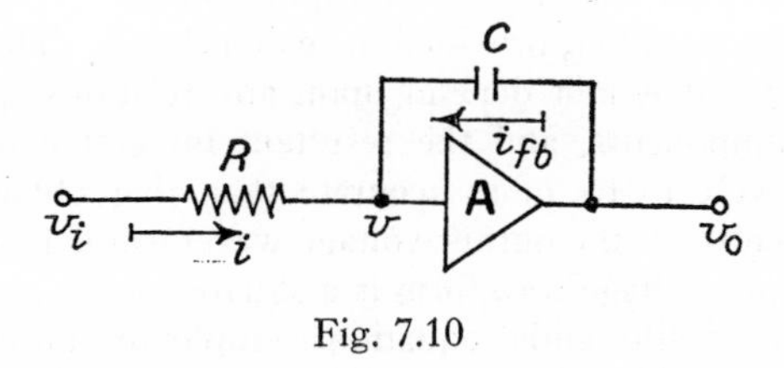

Fig. 7.10

Fig. 7.10 is the conventional flow diagram of an integrator stage employing a high gain d.c. amplifier. The voltages shown are with respect to earth which is not normally indicated in a flow diagram. The d.c. voltage amplifier has a high voltage gain, of the order of 10^4 or more.

It also has an odd number of stages in order to provide negative feed-back.

Now at the grid of the first stage of the d.c. amplifier, by Kirchhoff's first law:

$$i+i_{fb} = 0$$

$$\therefore \frac{v_i - v}{R} + \frac{v_o - v}{\dfrac{1}{pC}} = 0 \quad (1)$$

Now $v = -v_o/A$, the negative sign being due to the type of feed-back used.

$\therefore$ from equation (1) above,

$$\frac{v_i}{R} + \frac{v_o}{A}\left(\frac{1}{R} + pC\right) + pCv_o = 0$$

$$\therefore \frac{v_i}{R} = -pCv_o\left[\left(\frac{1}{ApRC} + \frac{1}{A}\right) + 1\right]$$

$$\therefore v_o = \frac{-\dfrac{1}{RC}\cdot\dfrac{1}{p}\cdot v_i}{1 + \dfrac{1}{A}\left(\dfrac{1}{pRC} + 1\right)}$$

$$= -\frac{1}{RC}\cdot\frac{1}{p}\cdot v_i \quad \text{As } A \to \infty$$

$$\therefore v_o = -\frac{1}{RC}\int_0^t v_i\, dt \quad \textit{Ans.} \quad (2)$$

The equation shown above indicates that the output voltage is proportional to the time integral of the input voltage. It is independent of the gain of the amplifier, provided the gain is large. The performance of this integrator does not depend upon any relationship between the passive RC components, and the resultant integrated output voltage waveform is likely to be more accurate than that obtained from the simple RC circuit, i.e. the output voltage waveform is likely to be more linear if the input voltage waveform is a square wave.

The solution of differential equations, employing an electronic analogue computer is achieved by the repeated process of integration. Re-arrangement of the differential equation gives:

$$\frac{d^2x}{dt^2} = -\frac{b}{a}\frac{dx}{dt} - \frac{c}{a}x$$

$$\therefore \quad \frac{\mathrm{d}x}{\mathrm{d}t} = \int_0^t \left[-\frac{b}{a}\frac{\mathrm{d}x}{\mathrm{d}t} - \frac{c}{a}x \right] \mathrm{d}t$$

and

$$x = \int_0^t \frac{\mathrm{d}x}{\mathrm{d}t}\,\mathrm{d}t$$

$$= \int_0^t \int_0^t \left[-\frac{b}{a}\frac{\mathrm{d}x}{\mathrm{d}t} - \frac{c}{a}x \right] \mathrm{d}t\,\mathrm{d}t$$

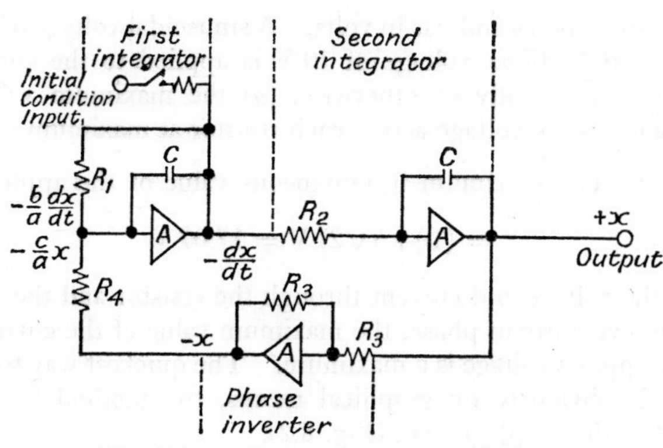

Fig. 7.11. Conventional flow diagram

The total input to the first integrator

$$= -\frac{b}{a}\cdot\frac{\mathrm{d}x}{\mathrm{d}t} - \frac{c}{a}\cdot x$$

the constants b/a and c/a being determined by resistors R_1 and R_4 respectively. The output from the first integrator is $-\mathrm{d}x/\mathrm{d}t$, the sign change being shown by equation (2). The second integrator has an input of $-\mathrm{d}x/\mathrm{d}t$, giving an output of $+x$. This output is then fed back via the phase inverter to produce $-x$, which by choice of R_4 gives $-(c/a)x$ as an input to the first integrator. The solution of the differential equation may be observed at the output on a slow speed C.R.O. or other suitable recording apparatus.

PAPER NO. VIII—JUNE, 1963

1. A 10·0 Ω fixed resistor is connected in series with another resistor for which the current/voltage relationship is:

$$i = 0{\cdot}002v^3$$

where i is in amperes and v is in volts. A sinusoidal voltage of 5 V r.m.s. in series with a direct voltage of 10 V is applied to the combination. Determine, graphically or otherwise, (*a*) the maximum value of the current and (*b*) the voltage across each resistor at maximum current.

Solution The maximum instantaneous value of the applied voltage

$$= (10+5\sqrt{2})\ \text{V} = 17{\cdot}07\ \text{V}$$

Since the voltage and current through the resistor and the non-linear device are evidently in phase, the maximum value of the current occurs when the applied voltage is a maximum. The quickest way to solve this problem is obviously by graphical means, the method being clearly indicated in the graph shown, (Fig. 8.2).

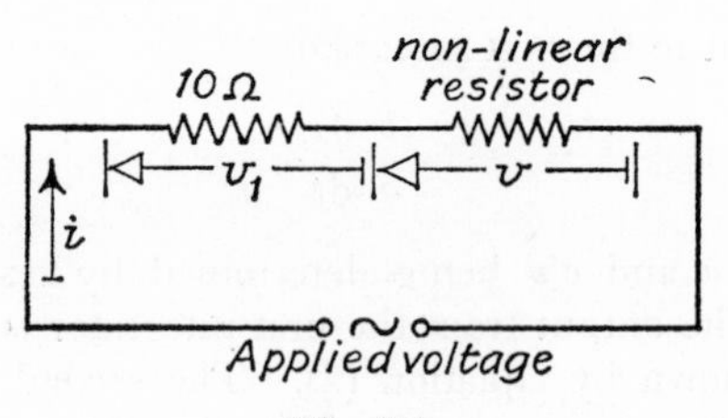

Fig. 8.1

(*a*) By inspection of the graph the maximum value of the current $= 0{\cdot}93$ A *Ans.*

(*b*) The voltage across the fixed resistor when maximum current is flowing $= 0{\cdot}93 \times 10 = 9{\cdot}3$ V *Ans.*

The voltage across the non-linear device when maximum current is flowing is given by:

$$v = \sqrt[3]{i/0{\cdot}002} = 10\sqrt[3]{0{\cdot}47} = 7{\cdot}75\ \text{V} \quad \textit{Ans.}$$

$$\simeq (17{\cdot}07-9{\cdot}3)\ \text{V}$$

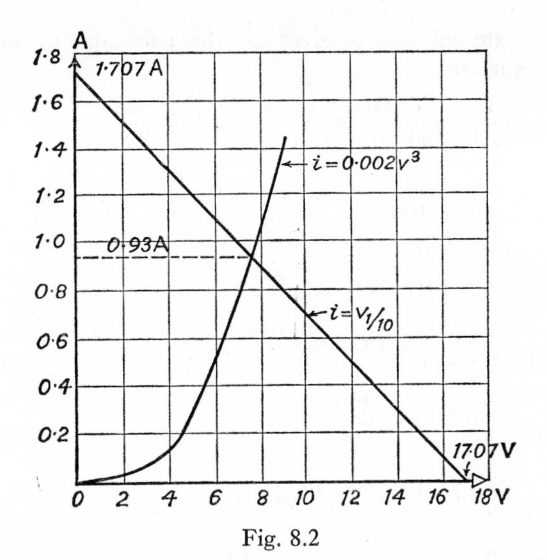

Fig. 8.2

2. A flywheel is driven by an electric motor and is made to follow the motion of an input wheel by means of an automatic control system. The torque applied to the flywheel is 10 Nm per milliradian of misalignment between the input wheel and the flywheel. The inclusive moment of inertia of the flywheel is 100 kg-m^2 and there is a viscous-frictional torque on the flywheel of 1000 Nm per rad/s. The input wheel is maintained in sinusoidal angular oscillation through $\pm 30°$ about a mean position with an angular frequency $\omega = 1$ rad/s.

Set up the differential equation of the system in terms of the angle of misalignment and the input angle and derive the steady-state solution of the equation. From the solution calculate the peak value of the misalignment angle and the time phase relation between the misalignment and the input.

Solution For the definition of the terms and the derivation of the differential equation see Paper No. IV—June 1961, question No. 7, page 61.

$$\therefore\ J\frac{d^2\theta_o}{dt^2}+F\frac{d\theta_o}{dt}+K\theta_o = K\theta_i$$

In this case $\theta_i = F(t) = \pi/6 \sin t$, since $\omega = 1$ rad/s. Also $J = 100$ kg-m^2; $F = 1000$ Nm per rad/s, and $K = 10$ Nm/milliradian $= 10.10^3$ Nm/rad.

$$\therefore\ 100\frac{d^2\theta_o}{dt^2}+1000\frac{d\theta_o}{dt}+10{,}000\ \theta_o = 10{,}000\ (\pi/6)\sin t$$

$$\therefore\ \frac{d^2\theta_o}{dt^2}+10\frac{d\theta_o}{dt}+100\ \theta_o = 100\ (\pi/6)\sin t$$

The steady state solution is given by the particular integral of the differential equation

$$= \frac{1}{D^2+10D+100} \frac{100\pi}{6} \sin t \quad \text{where } D = \frac{d}{dt}$$

$$= \frac{1}{(-1^2)+10D+100} \frac{100\pi}{6} \sin t \quad \text{since } \frac{1}{f(D^2)} \cdot \sin \omega t = \frac{1}{f(-\omega^2)} \cdot \sin \omega t$$

$$= \frac{1(10D-99)}{(10D+99)(10D-99)} \frac{100\pi}{6} \sin t$$

$$= \frac{1}{100(-1^2)-99^2} (10D-99) \frac{100\pi}{6} \sin t$$

$$= \frac{1}{9901} (-10D+99) \frac{100\pi}{6} \sin t$$

$$= \frac{1}{9901} \frac{100\pi}{6} (-10 \cos t + 99 \sin t)$$

$$= \frac{100\pi\sqrt{9901}}{9901 \times 6} \left(\sin t \frac{99}{\sqrt{9901}} - \frac{10}{\sqrt{9901}} \cos t \right)$$

$$\therefore \theta_o = 0{\cdot}526 \sin (t-\alpha) \quad \text{where } \alpha = \tan^{-1}\left(+\frac{10}{99}\right) \quad \textit{Ans.}$$

The peak value of the misalignment angle is evidently the steady state angular lag

$$= \alpha = \tan^{-1}\frac{10}{99} = 5^\circ 46' \quad \textit{Ans.}$$

$$\text{The misalignment} = \theta_i - \theta_o = \frac{\pi}{6} \sin t - 0{\cdot}526 \sin (t-\alpha)$$

$$\simeq \frac{\pi}{6} [\sin t - \sin (t-\alpha)]$$

$$= \frac{\pi}{3} \sin \alpha \cos (2t-\alpha)$$

$$\simeq 0{\cdot}1065 \cos (2t-\alpha) \text{ rad}$$

Hence from the equation above, the angular frequency of misalignment is twice that of the input, i.e. angular frequency of misalignment (2 *rad/s*) = *twice the angular frequency of the input* (1 *rad/s*). *Ans.*

3. A non-sinusoidal periodic voltage is applied to a circuit and causes a non-sinusoidal periodic current to flow. Develop an expression for the power dissipated in the circuit.

An uncompensated electrodynamic wattmeter reads 250 W when direct currents of 1·0 A and 0·05 A flow in its current and voltage coils respectively. Calculate the reading of the wattmeter when a current of

$$[10 \sin (314t+15°)+5 \sin 628t+4 \sin 1256t] \text{ amperes}$$

flows in the current coil and the voltage applied to the voltage coil circuit is

$$[400 \cos (314t-30°)+150 \sin (628t+15°)+100 \sin 942t] \text{ volts.}$$

The inductance of the voltage coil circuit is negligible. What is the resistance of the voltage coil circuit?

Solution Let the instantaneous value of the voltage applied to a circuit

$$= v = V_0+V_1 \sin \omega t+V_2 \sin (2\omega t+\theta_2)+V_3 \sin (3\omega t+\theta_3)+\cdots \quad (1)$$

The corresponding instantaneous value of the current

$$= i = I_0+I_1 \sin (\omega t-\phi_1)+I_2 \sin (2\omega t+\theta_2-\phi_2) + I_3 \sin (3\omega t+\theta_3-\phi_3)+\cdots \quad (2)$$

where $\phi_1, \phi_2, \phi_3, \ldots$ are the angles of lag, or lead, in this case assumed lag, of the currents $I_1, I_2, I_3, \ldots$ with respect to the voltages $V_1, V_2, V_3, \ldots$

The instantaneous value of the power is then:

$$\begin{aligned} vi &= V_0I_0+V_1I_1 \sin \omega t \sin (\omega t-\phi_1) \\ &\quad + V_2I_2 \sin (2\omega t+\theta_2) \sin (2\omega t+\theta_2-\phi_2) \\ &\quad + V_3I_3 \sin (3\omega t+\theta_3) \sin (3\omega t+\theta_3-\phi_3) \\ &\quad + \cdots \\ &= V_0I_0+\tfrac{1}{2}V_1I_1\{\cos \phi_1-\cos (2\omega t-\phi_1)\} \\ &\quad + \tfrac{1}{2}V_2I_2\{\cos \phi_2-\cos (4\omega t+2\theta_2-\phi_2)\} \\ &\quad + \tfrac{1}{2}V_3I_3\{\cos \phi_3-\cos (6\omega t+2\theta_3-\phi_3)\} \\ &\quad + \cdots \end{aligned}$$

The average value of vi taken over a complete period, i.e. $0 < \omega t < 2\pi$ is called the power in the circuit, i.e.

$$\text{power} = \frac{1}{2\pi}\int_0^{2\pi} vi \, d(\omega t)$$

Now the average values of terms containing $\cos (2\omega t-\phi_1)$, $\cos (4\omega t+2\theta_2-\phi_2), \ldots$ is zero, and all the other product terms, i.e. $\sin \omega t$, $\sin (2\omega t+\theta_2-\phi_2)$, being periodic sinusoidal have average values of zero.

∴ The power in the circuit

$$= V_0I_0+\tfrac{1}{2}V_1I_1\cos\phi_1+\tfrac{1}{2}V_2I_2\cos\phi_2+\tfrac{1}{2}V_3I_3\cos\phi_3+\dots \qquad (3)$$

Now $\dfrac{V_1}{\sqrt{2}} = V_{1\text{ r.m.s.}}$ and $\dfrac{I_1}{\sqrt{2}} = I_{1\text{ r.m.s.}}$

∴ The total power

$$= V_0I_0+V_{1\text{ r.m.s.}}I_{1\text{ r.m.s.}}\cos\phi_1+V_{2\text{ r.m.s.}}I_{2\text{ r.m.s.}}\cos\phi_2$$
$$+V_{3\text{ r.m.s.}}I_{3\text{ r.m.s.}}\cos\phi_3+\cdots$$

= the sum of the powers due to each individual frequency component of the complex voltage and current waveform.

Numerical portion

Since the wattmeter is an uncompensated electrodynamic type it will be affected by all components of frequency.

Given $v = 400\cos(314t-30°)+150\sin(628t+15°)+100\sin 942t$

$$= 400\sin(100\pi t+60°)+150\sin(200\pi t+15°)+100\sin 300\pi t$$

and $i = 10\sin(314t+15°)+5\sin 628t+4\sin 1256t$

$$= 10\sin(100\pi t+15°)+5\sin 200\pi t+4\sin 400\pi t$$

∴ from equation (1), the total power indicated by the wattmeter

$$= \tfrac{1}{2}400\times 10\cos 45°+\tfrac{1}{2}150\times 5\cos 15°$$

$$= 2000\times 0{\cdot}707+375\times 0{\cdot}9659$$

$$= 1777\text{ W} \quad \textit{Ans.}$$

There being no corresponding component of current at $\omega = 300\pi$, this will give no power; similarly for $\omega = 400\pi$, since there is no corresponding component of voltage.

Under d.c. conditions the power indicated by the wattmeter

$$= 250\text{ W} = V_0I_0 = Ir\times I_0$$

where I is the current in the voltage coil, and r is its resistance.

$$= 0{\cdot}05r\times 1{\cdot}0$$

$$\therefore\ r = \frac{250}{0{\cdot}05} = 5\text{ k}\Omega \quad \textit{Ans.}$$

4. A wire-wound resistor for use in a resistance box for audio frequencies has a resistance $R = 10{,}000\ \Omega$, a residual self-inductance of $L = 2$ mH and a residual self-capacitance equivalent to a capacitor $C = 30$ pF connected across the terminals of the resistor. Derive approximate expressions in terms of R, L, C, and the angular frequency ω for the impedance and time-constant of the resistor. Justify the approximations made.

Assuming that the ohmic resistance of the wire is independent of frequency, calculate the effective resistance and the phase-angle error of the resistor when the frequency is 100 kc/s.

Solution The resistor may be represented by an equivalent circuit consisting of a resistor R_{eq} in series with a reactor X_{eq}.

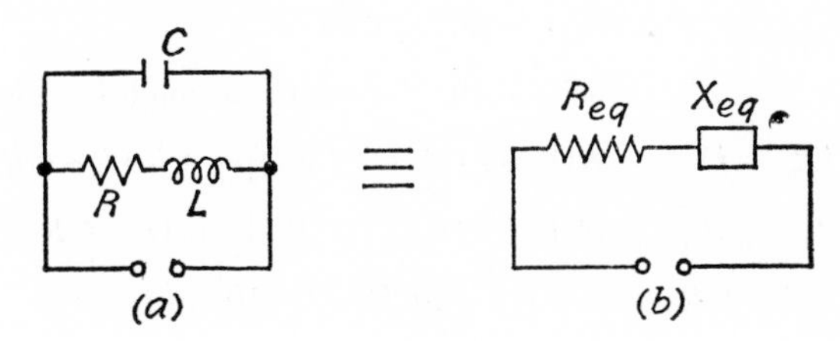

Fig. 8.3

$$\therefore\ \mathbf{Z} = R_{eq}+jX_{eq} = \frac{\left(R+j\omega L\right)\left(\frac{-j}{\omega C}\right)}{R+j\left(\omega L-\frac{1}{\omega C}\right)}$$

$$= \frac{\frac{L}{C}-j\frac{R}{\omega C}}{R+j\left(\omega L+\frac{1}{\omega C}\right)}$$

$$= \frac{\omega L-jR}{\omega CR+j(\omega^2 LC-1)}$$

$$= \frac{(\omega L-jR)[\omega CR-j(\omega^2 LC-1)]}{\omega^2 C^2 R^2+(\omega^2 LC-1)^2} \quad \text{by rationalization}$$

$$= \frac{[\omega^2 LCR-R(\omega^2 LC-1)] + j[-\omega CR^2-\omega L(\omega^2 LC-1)]}{\omega^2 C^2 R^2+\omega^4 L^2 C^2-2\omega^2 LC+1}$$

$$= \frac{R+j\omega(L-CR^2-\omega^2 L^2 C)}{1-\omega^2 C(2L-CR^2)+\omega^4 L^2 C^2} \qquad (1)$$

Now we are given $R = 10^4\ \Omega$, $L = 2.10^{-3}$ H, $C = 30.10^{-12}$ and ω is in the audio frequency range, i.e. 30 c/s–30 kc/s approximately.

$$\therefore\ \omega L = \omega.2.10^{-3} \ll R = 10^4$$

and
$$\omega C = \omega.30.10^{-12} \ll R = 10^4$$

$$\therefore\ \omega^4 L^2 C^2 \ll 1{\cdot}0 \quad \text{and} \quad \omega^2 L^2 C \ll L$$

$\therefore$ From equation (1),

$$R_{eq}+jX_{eq} = \frac{R}{1-\omega^2 C(2L-CR^2)}+j\omega\frac{L-CR^2}{1-\omega^2 C(2L-CR^2)}$$

Now

$$\begin{aligned}\omega^2 C(2L-CR^2) &= \omega^2\times 30.10^{-12}(4.10^{-3}-30.10^{-12}\times 10^8)\\ &= \omega^2\times 3.10^{-11}\times 10^{-3}\\ &= \omega^2\times 3.10^{-14} \quad \text{which is much less than unity}\end{aligned}$$

$$\therefore\ R_{eq}+jX_{eq} = R[1-\omega^2 C(2L-CR^2)]^{-1}+j\omega(L-CR^2)$$

$$\therefore\ R_{eq}+j\omega L_{eq} = R[1+\omega^2 C(2L-CR^2)]+j\omega(L-CR^2)$$

Now
$$L-CR^2 = 2.10^{-3}-30.10^{-12}\times 10^8 = -10^{-3}$$

$$\therefore\ R_{eq}+j\omega L_{eq} = R[1+\omega^2 C(2L-CR^2)]-j\omega(CR^2-L) \qquad (2)$$

Also since
$$\omega^2 C(2L-CR^2) \ll 1{\cdot}0$$

$$\mathbf{Z} = R_{eq}+j\omega L_{eq} = R-j\omega(CR^2-L) \quad \textit{Ans.}$$

Now the time constant is defined as L_{eq}/R_{eq}

$$\therefore\ \text{time constant } \tau \simeq \frac{CR^2-L}{R} \quad \textit{Ans.}$$

At 100 kc/s, from equation (2),

$$\begin{aligned}\mathbf{Z} &= 10^4[1+4\pi^2.10^{10}\times 30.10^{-12}\times 10^{-3}]-j2\pi.10^5\times 10^{-3}\\ &= 10^4[1+12\pi^2.10^{-4}]-j2\pi.10^2\\ &\simeq 10^4-j2\pi.10^2\\ &\simeq 10^2(10^2-j2\pi)\end{aligned}$$

$$\begin{aligned}\therefore\ Z &= 10^2\sqrt{10^4+4\pi^2}\\ &= 10{,}020\ \Omega = \text{the effective resistance} \quad \textit{Ans.}\end{aligned}$$

Note: since $Z \simeq 10{,}000\ \Omega$ to slide rule accuracy, the above answer is only accurate to within limitations of the log tables.

The phase angle error is defined as

$$\tan^{-1}\frac{\omega L_{eq}}{R_{eq}} = \tan^{-1}\frac{\omega(L-CR^2-\omega^2CL^2)}{R}$$

$$= \tan^{-1}\frac{\omega(CR^2-L)}{R}\text{ lead}$$

$$= \tan^{-1}\frac{2\pi.10^5\times 10^{-3}}{10^4}$$

$$= \tan^{-1} 2\pi.10^{-2}$$

$$= 3^\circ{\cdot}36'\text{ lead} \quad \textit{Ans.}$$

5. An impedance Z is extracted from each of the four arms of a symmetrical lattice network, and Z is placed in series with one of the input and also one of the output terminals of the network. Show that the resulting arrangement is electrically identical with the original lattice network.

Hence indicate how this rearrangement might be used to obtain the equivalent T-network for a given symmetrical lattice network.

Solution This problem may be solved by means of the fact that electrically identical networks have the same characteristic impedances and propagation constants. The tedious application of Kirchhoff's laws to the networks will eventually show that they are identical. The following method is suggested as being more direct.

Electrically identical networks have the same **A, B, C, D** *constants*

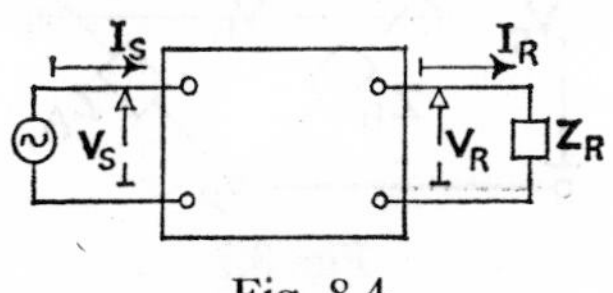

Fig. 8.4

Now $\quad\quad \mathbf{V_S} = \mathbf{AV_R}+\mathbf{BI_R}$

and $\quad\quad \mathbf{I_S} = \mathbf{CV_R}+\mathbf{DI_R}$

or putting in matrix equation form:

$$\begin{bmatrix}\mathbf{V_S}\\ \mathbf{I_S}\end{bmatrix} = \begin{bmatrix}\mathbf{A} & \mathbf{B}\\ \mathbf{C} & \mathbf{D}\end{bmatrix}\begin{bmatrix}\mathbf{V_R}\\ \mathbf{I_R}\end{bmatrix}$$

where $\mathbf{A} = \dfrac{\mathbf{V_S}}{\mathbf{V_R}}$ with the termination on open circuit

$\mathbf{B} = \dfrac{\mathbf{V_S}}{\mathbf{I_R}}$ with the termination on short circuit

$\mathbf{C} = \dfrac{\mathbf{I_S}}{\mathbf{V_R}}$ with the termination on open circuit

$\mathbf{D} = \dfrac{\mathbf{I_S}}{\mathbf{I_R}}$ with the termination on short circuit

To show that:

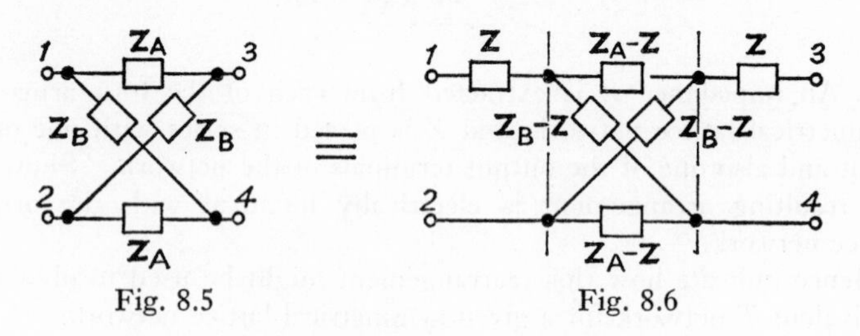

Fig. 8.5 Fig. 8.6

For convenience, Fig. 8.5 is shown redrawn as in Fig. 8.7.

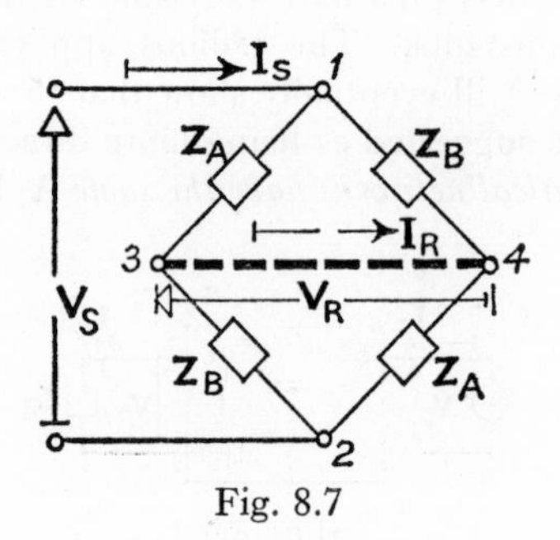

Fig. 8.7

With terminals 3 and 4 on open circuit,

$$\mathbf{V_R} = \mathbf{I_S}/2(\mathbf{Z_A} - \mathbf{Z_B}) = \frac{\mathbf{V_S}}{\mathbf{Z_A} + \mathbf{Z_B}} \cdot (\mathbf{Z_A} - \mathbf{Z_B})$$

$$\therefore\ \mathbf{A} = \frac{\mathbf{V_S}}{\mathbf{V_R}} = \frac{\mathbf{Z_A} + \mathbf{Z_B}}{\mathbf{Z_A} - \mathbf{Z_B}}$$

and

$$\mathbf{C} = \frac{\mathbf{I_S}}{\mathbf{V_R}} = \frac{2}{\mathbf{Z_A} - \mathbf{Z_B}}$$

With the terminals 3 and 4 on short circuit,

$$\mathbf{I_R} = \frac{\text{open circuit voltage between 3 and 4}}{\text{looking in impedance between 3 and 4 with 1 and 2 short circuited}} \quad \text{(By Thévenin's Theorem)}$$

$$= \mathbf{V_S}\frac{\mathbf{Z_A}-\mathbf{Z_B}}{\mathbf{Z_A}+\mathbf{Z_B}}\frac{\mathbf{Z_A}+\mathbf{Z_B}}{2\mathbf{Z_A}\mathbf{Z_B}}$$

$$\therefore \mathbf{B} = \frac{\mathbf{V_S}}{\mathbf{I_R}} = \frac{2\mathbf{Z_A}\mathbf{Z_B}}{\mathbf{Z_A}-\mathbf{Z_B}}$$

Also

$$\mathbf{V_S} = \mathbf{I_R}\frac{2\mathbf{Z_A}\mathbf{Z_B}}{\mathbf{Z_A}-\mathbf{Z_B}} = \mathbf{I_S}\frac{2\mathbf{Z_A}\mathbf{Z_B}}{\mathbf{Z_A}+\mathbf{Z_B}}$$

$$\therefore \mathbf{D} = \frac{\mathbf{I_S}}{\mathbf{I_R}} = \frac{\mathbf{Z_A}+\mathbf{Z_B}}{\mathbf{Z_A}-\mathbf{Z_B}} = \mathbf{A}$$

Hence the matrix equation for the original lattice network is:

$$\begin{bmatrix}\mathbf{V_S}\\ \mathbf{I_S}\end{bmatrix} = \begin{bmatrix}\dfrac{\mathbf{Z_A}+\mathbf{Z_B}}{\mathbf{Z_A}-\mathbf{Z_B}} & \dfrac{2\mathbf{Z_A}\mathbf{Z_B}}{\mathbf{Z_A}-\mathbf{Z_B}}\\ \dfrac{2}{\mathbf{Z_A}-\mathbf{Z_B}} & \dfrac{\mathbf{Z_A}+\mathbf{Z_B}}{\mathbf{Z_A}-\mathbf{Z_B}}\end{bmatrix}\begin{bmatrix}\mathbf{V_R}\\ \mathbf{I_R}\end{bmatrix}$$

$$= \frac{1}{\mathbf{Z_A}-\mathbf{Z_B}}\begin{bmatrix}\mathbf{Z_A}+\mathbf{Z_B} & 2\mathbf{Z_A}\mathbf{Z_B}\\ 2 & \mathbf{Z_A}+\mathbf{Z_B}\end{bmatrix}\begin{bmatrix}\mathbf{V_R}\\ \mathbf{I_R}\end{bmatrix} \quad (1)$$

The matrix equation for the network in Fig. 8.6, between the dashed lines, is evidently found by putting $\mathbf{Z_A}-\mathbf{Z}$ and $\mathbf{Z_B}-\mathbf{Z}$ for $\mathbf{Z_A}$ and $\mathbf{Z_B}$ respectively in equation (1).

$$\begin{bmatrix}\mathbf{V_S}'\\ \mathbf{I_S}'\end{bmatrix} = \frac{1}{\mathbf{Z_A}-\mathbf{Z_B}}\begin{bmatrix}(\mathbf{Z_A}+\mathbf{Z_B}-2\mathbf{Z}) & 2(\mathbf{Z_A}-\mathbf{Z})(\mathbf{Z_B}-\mathbf{Z})\\ 2 & (\mathbf{Z_A}+\mathbf{Z_B}-2\mathbf{Z})\end{bmatrix}\begin{bmatrix}\mathbf{V_R}'\\ \mathbf{I_R}'\end{bmatrix}$$

The dashes indicating input and output conditions for this network.

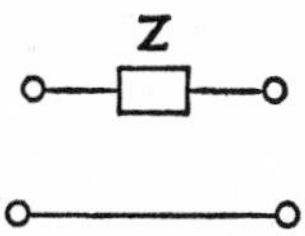

Fig. 8.8

The matrix bracket for the network shown in Fig. 8.8 is:

$$\begin{bmatrix}1 & \mathbf{Z}\\ 0 & 1\end{bmatrix}$$

∴ For the modified network,

$$\begin{bmatrix} \mathbf{V_S} \\ \mathbf{I_S} \end{bmatrix} = \frac{1}{\mathbf{Z_A}-\mathbf{Z_B}} \begin{bmatrix} 1 & \mathbf{Z} \\ 0 & 1 \end{bmatrix} \begin{bmatrix} \mathbf{Z_A}+\mathbf{Z_B}-2\mathbf{Z} & 2(\mathbf{Z_A}-\mathbf{Z})(\mathbf{Z_B}-\mathbf{Z}) \\ 2 & \mathbf{Z_A}+\mathbf{Z_B}-2\mathbf{Z} \end{bmatrix} \begin{bmatrix} 1 & \mathbf{Z} \\ 0 & 1 \end{bmatrix} \begin{bmatrix} \mathbf{V_R} \\ \mathbf{I_R} \end{bmatrix}$$

$$= \frac{1}{\mathbf{Z_A}-\mathbf{Z_B}} \begin{bmatrix} \mathbf{Z_A}+\mathbf{Z_B} & 2(\mathbf{Z_A}-\mathbf{Z})(\mathbf{Z_B}-\mathbf{Z}) + \mathbf{Z}(\mathbf{Z_A}+\mathbf{Z_B}-2\mathbf{Z}) \\ 2 & \mathbf{Z_A}+\mathbf{Z_B}-2\mathbf{Z} \end{bmatrix} \begin{bmatrix} 1 & \mathbf{Z} \\ 0 & 1 \end{bmatrix} \begin{bmatrix} \mathbf{V_R} \\ \mathbf{I_R} \end{bmatrix}$$

$$= \frac{1}{\mathbf{Z_A}-\mathbf{Z_B}} \begin{bmatrix} \mathbf{Z_A}+\mathbf{Z_B} & 2\mathbf{Z_A}\mathbf{Z_B}-\mathbf{Z}\mathbf{Z_A}-\mathbf{Z}\mathbf{Z_B} \\ 2 & \mathbf{Z_A}+\mathbf{Z_B}-2\mathbf{Z} \end{bmatrix} \begin{bmatrix} 1 & \mathbf{Z} \\ 0 & 1 \end{bmatrix} \begin{bmatrix} \mathbf{V_R} \\ \mathbf{I_R} \end{bmatrix}$$

$$= \frac{1}{\mathbf{Z_A}-\mathbf{Z_B}} \begin{bmatrix} \mathbf{Z_A}+\mathbf{Z_B} & \mathbf{Z}(\mathbf{Z_A}+\mathbf{Z_B})+2\mathbf{Z_A}\mathbf{Z_B}-\mathbf{Z}\mathbf{Z_A}-\mathbf{Z}\mathbf{Z_B} \\ 2 & 2\mathbf{Z}+\mathbf{Z_A}+\mathbf{Z_B}-2\mathbf{Z} \end{bmatrix} \begin{bmatrix} \mathbf{V_R} \\ \mathbf{I_R} \end{bmatrix}$$

$$= \frac{1}{\mathbf{Z_A}-\mathbf{Z_B}} \begin{bmatrix} \mathbf{Z_A}+\mathbf{Z_B} & 2\mathbf{Z_A}\mathbf{Z_B} \\ 2 & \mathbf{Z_A}+\mathbf{Z_B} \end{bmatrix} \begin{bmatrix} \mathbf{V_R} \\ \mathbf{I_R} \end{bmatrix}$$

This is identical with matrix equation (1). Therefore the networks have the same **A, B, C, D** constants and are then electrically identical.

Equivalent of a lattice to a T-section

Since no restriction was placed on the impedance **Z**, that was extracted from each of the four arms of the symmetrical lattice network and placed in series with one of the input and also one of the output terminals of the network, **Z** can therefore be made equal to $\mathbf{Z_A}$. The result, as seen in the figures drawn below is a symmetrical, unbalanced T-section.

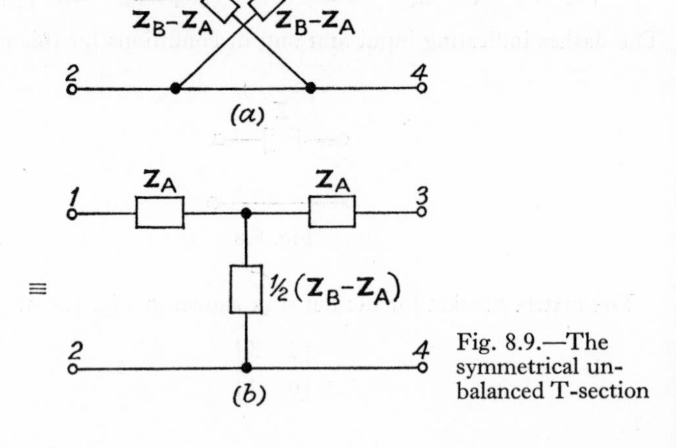

Fig. 8.9.—The symmetrical unbalanced T-section

6. The series loop inductance of a certain cable is small compared with the loop resistance at low frequencies, while the shunt leakance is small compared with the shunt capacitance. Show, from first principles, that at such frequencies the attenuation and wavelength coefficients approximate to values proportional to the square root of the operating frequency.

A cable has a loop resistance of 88 Ω per mile and a shunt capacitance of 0·06 μF per mile. Calculate for steady-state sine transmission at 50 c/s (*a*) the attenuation and phase-change coefficients and (*b*) the time of transmission over a 50-mile length of the cable.

Solution The propagation coefficient γ

$$= \sqrt{(R+j\omega L)(G+j\omega C)}$$

where $R\,\Omega$ is the loop resistance per unit length of cable,

LH is the loop inductance per unit length of cable,

G mhos is the shunt conductance per unit length of cable, and

C F is the shunt capacitance per unit length of cable.

$$\therefore\ \gamma = \sqrt{j\omega CR\left(1+j\frac{\omega L}{R}\right)\left(1+\frac{G}{j\omega C}\right)}$$

$$= \sqrt{j}\,\sqrt{\omega CR}\,\sqrt{\left(1+\frac{LG}{RC}\right)+j\omega\left(\frac{L}{R}-\frac{G}{\omega^2 C}\right)}$$

Now $L < R$ and $G < C$

$$\therefore\ \frac{LG}{RC} \ll 1{\cdot}0$$

and since ω is low, L/R is small,

and $$\frac{G}{\omega C} < 1{\cdot}0$$

$$\therefore\ \gamma \simeq \sqrt{j}\,\sqrt{\omega CR}\,\sqrt{1} \qquad (1)$$

Now $$j = \cos\frac{\pi}{2}+j\sin\frac{\pi}{2}$$

$$\therefore\ \text{the principle value of } \sqrt{j} = \cos\frac{\pi}{4}+j\sin\frac{\pi}{4}$$

$$\therefore\ \sqrt{j} = \frac{1}{\sqrt{2}}+j\frac{1}{\sqrt{2}}$$

Hence, from equation (1),

$$\gamma = \left(\frac{1}{\sqrt{2}}+j\frac{1}{\sqrt{2}}\right)\sqrt{\omega CR}$$

$$= \sqrt{\frac{CR}{2}}\cdot\sqrt{\omega}+j\sqrt{\frac{CR}{2}}\cdot\sqrt{\omega}$$

$$= \alpha+j\beta$$

where α = the attenuation coefficient, N; and β = the wavelength, or phase-change coefficient, rad.

Equating in-phase components,

$$\alpha = \sqrt{\frac{CR}{2}}\cdot\sqrt{\omega} = \sqrt{\pi CR}.\sqrt{f} \quad \text{since } \omega = 2\pi f$$

$\therefore$ The attenuation coefficient approximates to, a value proportional to $\sqrt{f}$, i.e. the square root of the operating frequency. Q.E.D.

Equating in-quadrature components,

$$\beta = \sqrt{\frac{CR}{2}}\cdot\sqrt{\omega} = \sqrt{\pi CR}.\sqrt{f} \text{ rad}$$

$\therefore$ The wavelength, or phase change coefficient approximates to a value proportional to $\sqrt{f}$, i.e. the square root of the operating frequency.

Q.E.D.

Given $R = 88\ \Omega$, $C = 0{\cdot}06\ \mu\text{F}$, $f = 50$ c/s

$$\therefore \alpha = \sqrt{\pi\times0{\cdot}06\times10^{-6}\times88\times50} = 0{\cdot}0288 \text{ neper/mile}$$

$$= 8{\cdot}686\times0{\cdot}0288 = 0{\cdot}25 \text{ db/mile} \quad \textit{Ans. (a)}$$

and

$$\beta = \sqrt{\pi\times0{\cdot}06\times10^{-6}\times88\times50}$$

$$= 0{\cdot}0288 \text{ rad/mile} \quad \textit{Ans. (a)}$$

(*b*) The distance along the line such that the phase change is 2π rad is called the wavelength λ

$$\therefore \lambda\beta = 2\pi \quad \text{or} \quad \lambda = \frac{2\pi}{\beta}$$

Now the velocity of propagation

$$v = f\lambda = \frac{2\pi f}{\beta} = \frac{\omega}{\beta}$$

$$\therefore\ v = \frac{2\pi \times 50}{0{\cdot}0288} \text{ miles per second}$$

$\therefore$ time of transmission over a 50-mile length of cable

$$= \frac{50 \times 0{\cdot}0288}{2\pi \times 50} \text{ s}$$

$$= \underline{4{\cdot}58 \text{ ms}} \quad \textit{Ans. (b)}$$

7. Give circuit arrangements, applicable to unbalanced 3-phase currents, which may be used in each of the following cases:

(*a*) to measure zero-sequence currents,
(*b*) to measure negative-sequence currents when zero-sequence currents are absent.

Illustrate your answer with vector diagrams and deduce the necessary circuit conditions in each case.

Solution

(*a*)

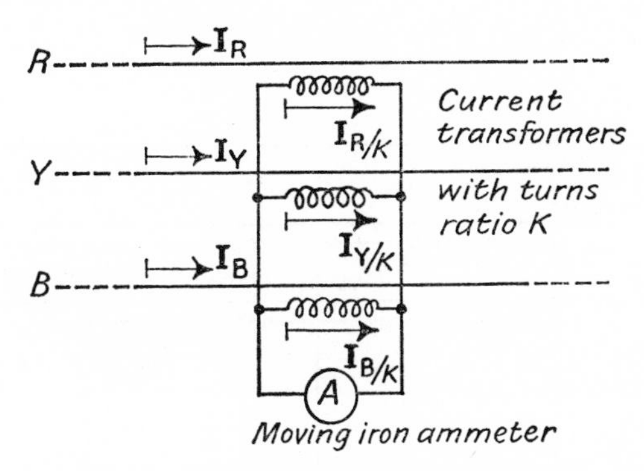

Fig. 8.10.—Circuit to measure zero-sequence currents

Assuming a phase sequence of *RYB*:

$$\mathbf{I_R} = \mathbf{I}_1 + \mathbf{I}_2 + \mathbf{I}_0 \tag{1}$$

$$\mathbf{I_Y} = a^2\mathbf{I}_1 + a\mathbf{I}_2 + \mathbf{I}_0 \tag{2}$$

$$\mathbf{I_B} = a\mathbf{I}_1 + a^2\mathbf{I}_2 + \mathbf{I}_0 \tag{3}$$

where $\mathbf{I}_1$ = the positive-sequence component of the line current,

$\mathbf{I}_2$ = the negative-sequence component of the line current,

$\mathbf{I}_0$ = the zero-sequence component of the line current.

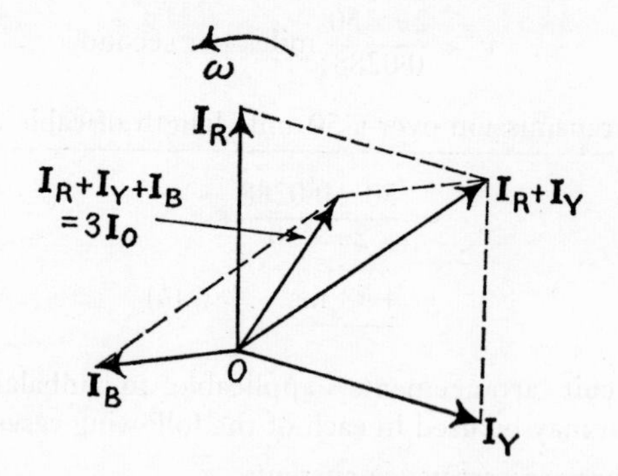

Fig. 8.11.—Vector diagram showing the sum of the three unbalanced line currents—phase sequence *RYB*

(*b*)

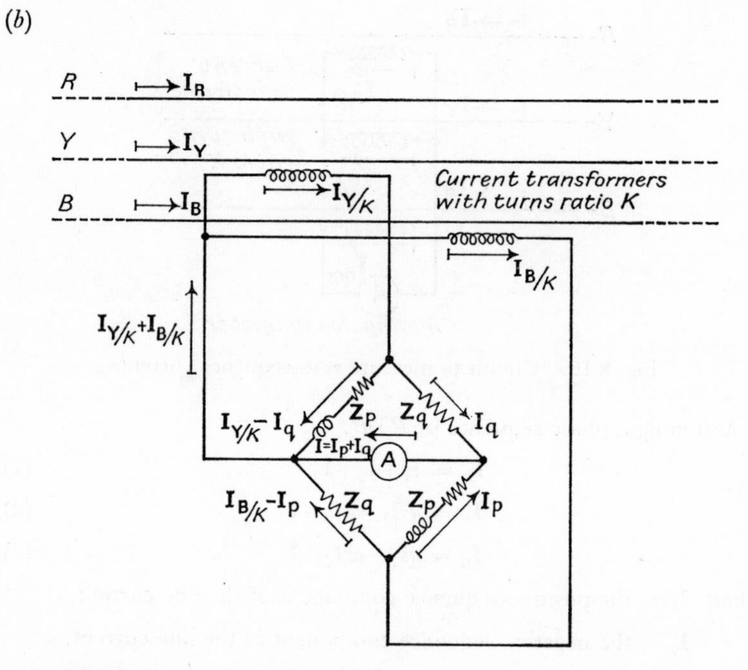

Fig. 8.12.—Circuit used to measure negative-sequence currents

Adding equations (1), (2), and (3),

$$\mathbf{I}_0 = \tfrac{1}{3}[\mathbf{I}_R+\mathbf{I}_Y+\mathbf{I}_B] \quad \text{since } 1+a+a^2 = 0$$

$$= \frac{K}{3}\left[\frac{\mathbf{I}_R}{K}+\frac{\mathbf{I}_Y}{K}+\frac{\mathbf{I}_B}{K}\right]$$

$$= \frac{K}{3}\times(\text{ammeter reading})$$

In order that $\mathbf{I}_0$ is to be present, the system must be 3-phase, 4-wire, since in a 3-wire system $\mathbf{I}_0 = \tfrac{1}{3}[\mathbf{I}_R+\mathbf{I}_Y+\mathbf{I}_B] = 0$. If the fourth wire, the neutral is available, $\mathbf{I}_0$ may be found directly by finding the neutral current, which is the vector sum of the three line currents. Hence $\mathbf{I}_0 = \tfrac{1}{3}\mathbf{I}_N$.

In order that zero-sequence components of current are to be absent the 3-phase system must be 3-wire, so that $\mathbf{I}_R+\mathbf{I}_Y+\mathbf{I}_B = 0$, therefore $\mathbf{I}_0 = 0$.

By inspection of the circuit diagram:

$$\mathbf{IZ} = (\mathbf{I}_Y/K-\mathbf{I}_q)\mathbf{Z}_p-\mathbf{I}_q\mathbf{Z}_q \tag{4}$$

and

$$\mathbf{IZ} = (\mathbf{I}_B/K-\mathbf{I}_p)\mathbf{Z}_q-\mathbf{I}_p\mathbf{Z}_p \tag{5}$$

where $\mathbf{Z}$ is the impedance of the ammeter.

Adding equations (4) and (5),

$$2\mathbf{IZ} = (\mathbf{I}_Y/K)\mathbf{Z}_p+(\mathbf{I}_B/K)\mathbf{Z}_q-(\mathbf{I}_p+\mathbf{I}_q)(\mathbf{Z}_p+\mathbf{Z}_q)$$

$$\therefore\ \mathbf{I} = \frac{(\mathbf{I}_Y/K)\mathbf{Z}_p+(\mathbf{I}_B/K)\mathbf{Z}_q}{2\mathbf{Z}+\mathbf{Z}_p+\mathbf{Z}_q} \tag{6}$$

$$= \frac{\frac{1}{K}(a^2\mathbf{I}_1+a\mathbf{I}_2)\mathbf{Z}_p+\frac{1}{K}(a\mathbf{I}_1+a^2\mathbf{I}_2)\mathbf{Z}_q}{2\mathbf{Z}+\mathbf{Z}_p+\mathbf{Z}_q} \quad \text{since } \mathbf{I}_0 = 0$$

$$= \frac{\frac{1}{K}\mathbf{I}_1(a^2\mathbf{Z}_p+a\mathbf{Z}_q)+\frac{1}{K}\mathbf{I}_2(a\mathbf{Z}_p+a^2\mathbf{Z}_q)}{2\mathbf{Z}+\mathbf{Z}_p+\mathbf{Z}_q} \tag{7}$$

Evidently if the ammeter is to indicate negative-sequence current then:

$$a^2\mathbf{Z}_p+a\mathbf{Z}_q = 0$$

$$\therefore\ \mathbf{Z}_p = \frac{-\mathbf{Z}_q}{a} = -a^2\mathbf{Z}_q$$

$$= \left(\frac{1}{2}+j\frac{\sqrt{3}}{2}\right)\mathbf{Z}_q \tag{8}$$

If $\mathbf{Z}_q$ is purely resistive, i.e. $\mathbf{Z}_q = R$, then evidently,

$$\mathbf{Z}_p = R\left(\frac{1}{2}+j\frac{\sqrt{3}}{2}\right)$$

i.e. a resistor $R/2\ \Omega$, in series with an inductive reactance $X = \frac{\sqrt{3}}{2} R\ \Omega$

Also

$$|\mathbf{Z}_p| = R = Z_q$$

∴ From equation (7),

$$I = \frac{\frac{1}{K}\mathbf{I}_2\mathbf{Z}_q(-a^3+a^2)}{2\mathbf{Z}+\mathbf{Z}_q(-a^2+1)}$$

$$= \underline{\frac{-\frac{1}{K}\mathbf{I}_2R(1-a^2)}{2\mathbf{Z}+R(1-a^2)}} \quad \text{since } a^3 = 1$$

Thus $\mathbf{I}_2$ may be found; however, if the ammeter impedance $\mathbf{Z}$ is small,

$$\mathbf{I} = \frac{-\frac{1}{K}\mathbf{I}_2R(1-a^2)}{R(1-a^2)}$$

$$= -\frac{1}{K}\mathbf{I}_2 \qquad (9)$$

$$\therefore \mathbf{I}_2 = -K\mathbf{I}$$

or

$$\underline{I_2 = KI = K \times \text{the ammeter reading}}$$

Now from equation (6),

$$\mathbf{I} = (\mathbf{I}_Y/K)\frac{R\left(\frac{1}{2}+j\frac{\sqrt{3}}{2}\right)}{R\left(\frac{3}{2}+j\frac{\sqrt{3}}{2}\right)}+(\mathbf{I}_B/K)\frac{R}{R\left(\frac{3}{2}+j\frac{\sqrt{3}}{2}\right)} \quad \text{assuming } Z = 0$$

$$= (\mathbf{I}_Y/K)\frac{\frac{1}{2}(3+j\sqrt{3})}{3}+(\mathbf{I}_B/K)\frac{\frac{1}{2}(3-j\sqrt{3})}{3}$$

$$\therefore 3\mathbf{I} = (\mathbf{I}_Y/K)\sqrt{3}\underline{/30^\circ}+(\mathbf{I}_B/K)\sqrt{3}\underline{/-30^\circ}$$

$$\therefore \sqrt{3}\mathbf{I} = (\mathbf{I}_Y/K)\underline{/30^\circ}+(\mathbf{I}_B/K)\underline{/-30^\circ}$$

$$= -\frac{1}{K}\mathbf{I}_2 . \sqrt{3} \quad \text{from equation (9)}$$

$$\therefore \sqrt{3}\mathbf{I}_2 = -\mathbf{I}_Y\underline{/30^\circ}-\mathbf{I}_B\underline{/-30^\circ} \qquad (10)$$

$$= \mathbf{I}_Y\underline{/210^\circ}+\mathbf{I}_B\underline{/150^\circ} \qquad (11)$$

Thus, from equation (10) $\sqrt{3}\,\mathbf{I}_2$ is the vector sum of $\mathbf{I}_Y$, reversed and rotated through 30° in an anticlockwise direction, and $\mathbf{I}_B$ reversed and rotated through 30° in a clockwise direction. This is in effect rotating $\mathbf{I}_Y$ through 210° in an anticlockwise direction, and $\mathbf{I}_B$ through 150° in an anticlockwise direction.

Note: from equations (1), (2), and (3),

$$\begin{aligned}3\mathbf{I}_2 &= \mathbf{I}_R + a^2\mathbf{I}_Y + a\mathbf{I}_B\\ &= -(\mathbf{I}_Y+\mathbf{I}_B)+a^2\mathbf{I}_Y+a\mathbf{I}_B \quad \text{since } \mathbf{I}_R+\mathbf{I}_Y+\mathbf{I}_B = 0\\ &= \mathbf{I}_Y(a^2-1)+\mathbf{I}_B(a-1)\\ &= \mathbf{I}_Y\left(-\frac{3}{2}-j\frac{\sqrt{3}}{2}\right)+\mathbf{I}_B\left(-\frac{3}{2}+j\frac{\sqrt{3}}{2}\right)\\ &= \mathbf{I}_Y\sqrt{3}\,\underline{/210^\circ}+\mathbf{I}_B\sqrt{3}\,\underline{/150^\circ}\end{aligned}$$

$$\therefore\ \sqrt{3}\mathbf{I}_2 = \mathbf{I}_Y\underline{/210^\circ}+\mathbf{I}_B\underline{/150^\circ} \qquad (12)$$

Equation (12), which is identical with equation (11), verifies the previous statement made about the rotations of the vectors $\mathbf{I}_Y$ and $\mathbf{I}_B$.

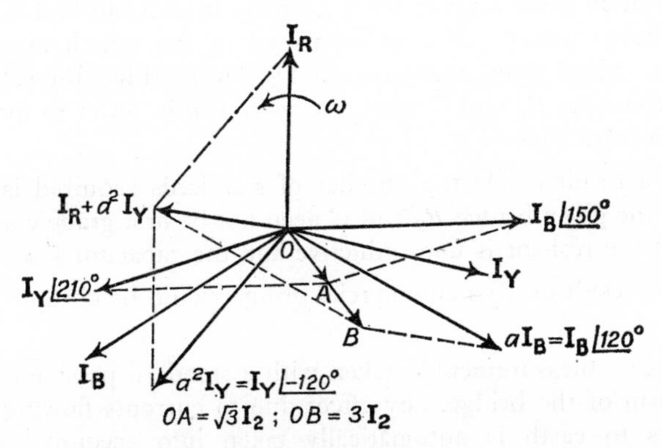

Fig. 8.13.—Vector diagram showing the determination of the negative-sequence current of the unbalanced line currents

8. Discuss the advantage of the substitution method applied to an a.c. bridge.

The bridge shown in Fig. 8.14 is used to measure the unknown capacitance C_x. The standard capacitor C_s is capable of step adjustment. A balance with C_x in circuit is achieved with $R_1 = 1000\ \Omega$.

When C_s, set at 0·1 μF, is inserted in place of C_x, balance is restored by increasing R_1 to 1030 Ω. Calculate the value of C_x.

If the value of R_1 is known to within 0·1%, what will be the uncertainty in the value determined for C_x?

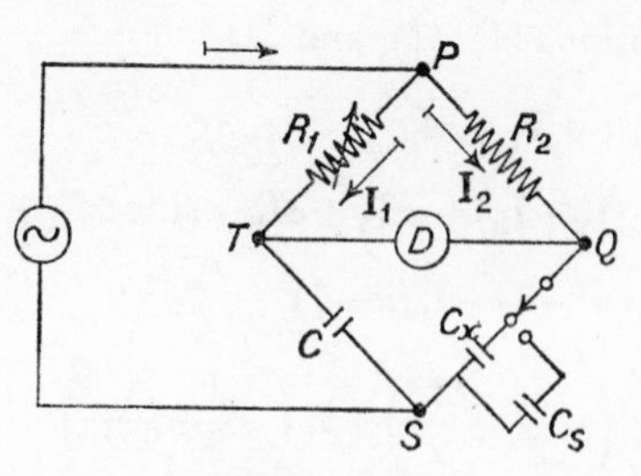

Fig. 8.14

Note: The conventional directions of current shown in Fig. 8.14 were not indicated in the original question.

Solution The advantages of the substitution method applied to an a.c. bridge may be summarized as follows:

1. It eliminates the need to know accurately the values of the passive elements of all three arms of the a.c. bridge in order to find the value of the unknown passive element contained in the fourth arm. In the particular bridge given, known as the De Sauty bridge, the values of the passive elements R_2 and C need not be known in order to measure the unknown capacitance C_x.

2. As a result of (1) the number of standards required is reduced. Thus in the given bridge R_2 and C need not be first grade components, provided the resistor is non-inductive and the capacitor loss-free.

3. As a result of (2) a commercial bridge would be cheaper to manufacture.

4. Since a measurement is taken with a standard passive component in one arm of the bridge, any effect due to currents flowing via stray capacities to earth is automatically taken into account. Thus the measurement of the unknown passive component will not be affected by currents flowing via the stray capacities to earth.

5. As a result of (5) the need for components to compensate for the currents flowing via the stray capacities to earth is eliminated. Thus the 'Wagner Earthing Device' is unnecessary.

6. The measurement may be made quite accurate by ensuring that the standard and unknown component are of the same order of

magnitude. Thus a small change in a component value will restore the bridge to balance.

At balance $\mathbf{V}_{PQ} = \mathbf{V}_{PT}$ and $\mathbf{V}_{QS} = \mathbf{V}_{TS}$

$$\therefore \mathbf{I}_2\mathbf{Z}_{PQ} = \mathbf{I}_1\mathbf{Z}_{PT} \text{ and } \mathbf{I}_2\mathbf{Z}_{QS} = \mathbf{I}_1\mathbf{Z}_{TS}$$

$$\therefore \mathbf{Z}_{PQ}.\mathbf{Z}_{TS} = \mathbf{Z}_{PT}.\mathbf{Z}_{QS}$$

$$\therefore R_2\left(\frac{-j}{\omega C}\right) = R_1\left(\frac{-j}{\omega C_x}\right)$$

$$\therefore \underline{C_x = \frac{R_1}{R_2}\cdot C} \qquad (1)$$

Also evidently $$C_s = \frac{R_1'}{R_2}\cdot C$$

where R_1' is the new value of R_1 for the bridge to balance with C_s in the circuit.

$$\therefore \frac{C_x}{C_s} = \frac{R_1 C}{R_2}\cdot\frac{R_2}{R_1' C} = \frac{R_1}{R_1'}$$

$$\therefore C_x = \frac{R_1}{R_1'}\cdot C_s$$

$$= \frac{1000}{1030}\cdot 0{\cdot}1\ \mu\text{F}$$

$$= \underline{0{\cdot}09709\ \mu\text{F}} \quad \textit{Ans.}$$

Now since R is known to within $0{\cdot}1\%$,

$$C_x = \frac{1000 \pm 0{\cdot}1\%}{1030 \pm 0{\cdot}1\%} \times 0{\cdot}1\ \mu\text{F}$$

$\therefore$ The largest value of

$$C_x = \frac{1000 + 0{\cdot}1\%}{1030 - 0{\cdot}1\%} \times 0{\cdot}1\ \mu\text{F}$$

$$= \frac{1001}{1028{\cdot}97} \times 0{\cdot}1\ \mu\text{F}$$

$$= \underline{0{\cdot}09729\ \mu\text{F}} \text{ by four-figure log. tables}$$

∴ The smallest value of

$$C_x = \frac{1000-0{\cdot}1\%}{1030+0{\cdot}1\%} \times 0{\cdot}1\ \mu F$$

$$= \frac{999}{1031{\cdot}03} \times 0{\cdot}1$$

$$= \underline{0{\cdot}09691\ \mu F}$$

∴ C_x may be $(0{\cdot}09729 - 0{\cdot}09709) = 0{\cdot}0002\ \mu F$ too large

or C_x may be $(0{\cdot}09709 - 0{\cdot}09691) = 0{\cdot}00018\ \mu F$ too small

∴ The uncertainty in the value of C_x may be:

$$\underline{+0{\cdot}0002\ \mu F} \quad \text{or} \quad \underline{-0{\cdot}00018\ \mu F} \quad \textit{Ans.}$$

$$\text{i.e. } +\frac{0{\cdot}0002}{0{\cdot}09709} \times 100\% \quad \text{or} \quad -\frac{0{\cdot}00018}{0{\cdot}09709} \times 100\%$$

$$= \underline{+0{\cdot}206\%} \quad \text{or} \quad \underline{-0{\cdot}20\%} \quad \textit{Ans.}$$

Aliter error $= \pm\frac{1000}{1030}(1{\cdot}001)(1{\cdot}001) \times 100\% = \pm 0{\cdot}20\%$

PAPER NO. IX—NOVEMBER, 1963

1. Explain what is meant by the iterative and image impedances of an asymmetrical 4-terminal network.

Calculate (*a*) the iterative impedances of the network of Fig. 9.1 and (*b*) the iterative coefficient for the network when connected between such impedances.

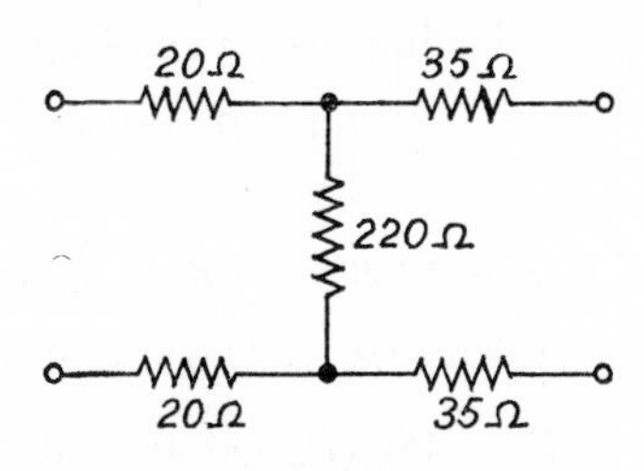

Fig. 9.1

Solution For the definitions of iterative and image impedances see Paper No. IV—June, 1961, question No. 3, page 51.

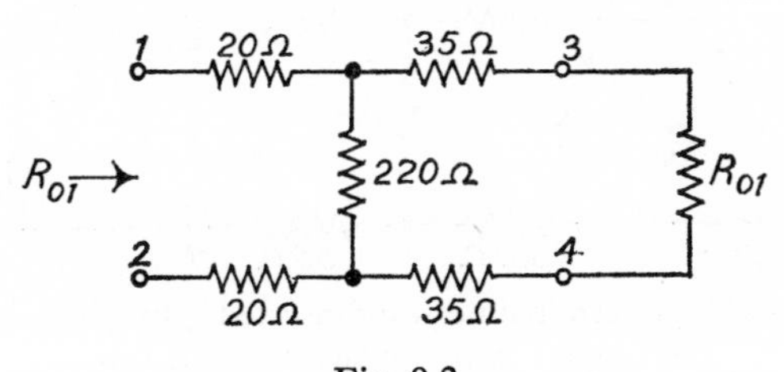

Fig. 9.2

By the definition of iterative impedance, and inspection of Fig. 9.2,

$$R_{01} = 40+\frac{(70+R_{01})220}{70+R_{01}+220}$$

$$\therefore\ 290R_{01}+R_{01}^2 = 11{,}600+40R_{01}+15{,}400+220R_{01}$$

$$\therefore\ R_{01}^2+30R_{01}-27{,}000 = 0$$

$$\therefore\ (R_{01}-150)(R_{01}+180) = 0$$

$\therefore$ The iterative impedance $R_{01} = \underline{150\ \Omega}$

and the iterative impedance $R_{03} = \underline{180\ \Omega}$ } *Ans.* (*a*)

Check

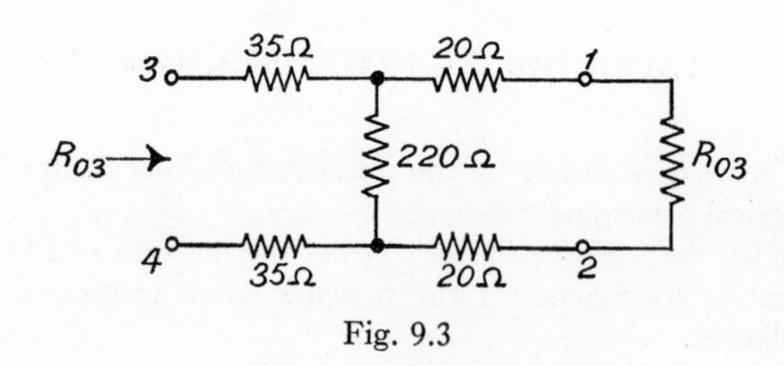

Fig. 9.3

By the definition of iterative impedance and inspection of Fig. 9.3:

$$R_{03} = 70+\frac{(40+R_{03})220}{40+R_{03}+220}$$

$$\therefore\ 260R_{03}+R_{03}^{\ 2} = 18{,}200+70R_{03}+8{,}800+220R_{03}$$

$$\therefore\ R_{03}^{\ 2}-30R_{03}-27{,}000 = 0$$

$$\therefore\ (R_{03}-180)(R_{01}+150) = 0$$

$$\therefore\ \text{The iterative impedance } R_{03} = 180\ \Omega$$

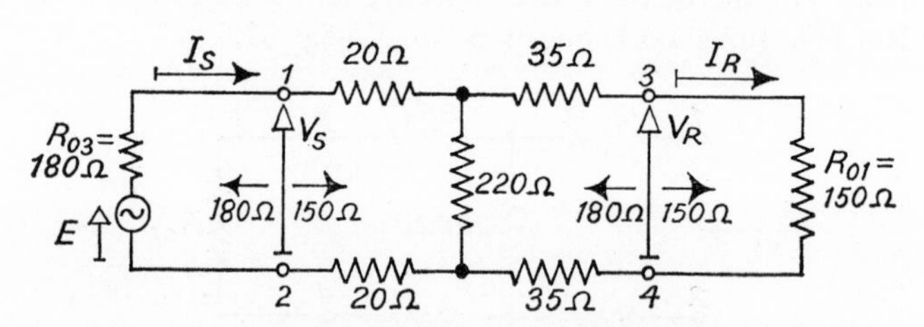

Fig. 9.4.—The 4-terminal network inserted between its iterative impedances with a generator of E volt

Since $\quad \dfrac{V_S}{I_S} = \dfrac{V_R}{I_R} = R_{01}$, by inspection of Fig. 9.4,

$$\therefore\ \frac{V_S}{V_R} = \frac{I_S}{I_R}$$

Hence the iterative propagation coefficient γ is given by:

$$\varepsilon^{\gamma} = \frac{I_S}{I_R} = \frac{V_S}{V_R}$$

Note: the term 'transfer constant' is sometimes used instead of iterative propagation coefficient. The latter equation does not hold in the case of networks inserted between their image impedances, when the term 'image transfer constant' is given by $\varepsilon^{\gamma} = \sqrt{V_S I_S / V_R I_R}$.

Now
$$I_S = \frac{E}{180+150} = \frac{E}{330} \text{ A}$$

The load current I_R may be found by means of Thévenin's Theorem.

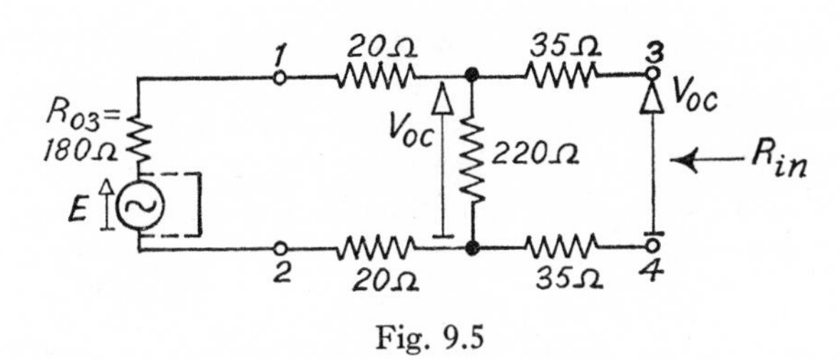

Fig. 9.5

By inspection of Fig. 9.5, $R_{in} = R_{03} = 180\ \Omega$ with the generator E replaced by a short circuit. Evidently,

$$V_{oc} = \frac{E\times 220}{180+40+220} = \frac{E\times 220}{440}$$

$$\therefore\ I_R = \frac{E\times 220}{440}\times\frac{1}{180+150} = \frac{E}{660} \text{ A}$$

$$\therefore\ \varepsilon^{\gamma} = \frac{I_S}{I_R} = \frac{E}{330}\times\frac{660}{E} = 2$$

$$\therefore\ \gamma = \ln 2 \text{ neper} \quad \text{or} \quad 20 \log 2 \text{ db}$$

$\therefore$ <u>The iterative propagation coefficient $\gamma = 6$ db</u> *Ans.* (*b*)

If the generator E were placed in series with R_{01} and R_{03} was considered as the load, the solution to the problem would remain unchanged, i.e. $\gamma = 6$ db. (The Theorem of Reciprocity applies.)

2. The primary and secondary windings of a transformer each have a total inductance of 2·5 H, and a resistance of 100 Ω. The mutual inductance between the windings is 1·5 H. The secondary winding is short-circuited and the primary winding is suddenly connected to a 100 V d.c. supply of negligible impedance. Derive expressions for the primary and secondary currents, and calculate the time at which the secondary current attains its maximum value. Sketch the approximate time variation of the two currents.

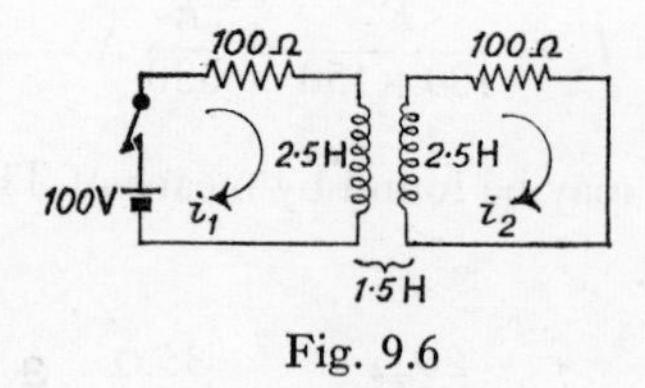

Fig. 9.6

Solution Using Maxwell's circulating current system, and assuming that the e.m.f. induced in the primary by virtue of current flowing in the secondary is $+M\,\mathrm{d}i/\mathrm{d}t$, since no information is given about the directions of the windings, then:

$$\frac{5}{2}\cdot\frac{di_1}{dt}+100i_1+\frac{3}{2}\cdot\frac{di_2}{dt} = 100 \tag{1}$$

and

$$\frac{5}{2}\cdot\frac{di_2}{dt}+100i_2+\frac{3}{2}\cdot\frac{di_1}{dt} = 0 \tag{2}$$

$$\therefore\ 5\frac{di_1}{dt}+200i_1+3\frac{di_2}{dt} = 200 \tag{3}$$

and

$$5\frac{di_2}{dt}+200i_2+3\frac{di_1}{dt} = 0 \tag{4}$$

Taking Laplace transforms of equations (3) and (4):

$$\therefore\ 5s\bar{\imath}_1-5i_1(0)+200\bar{\imath}_1+3s\bar{\imath}_2-3i_2(0) = \frac{200}{s} \tag{5}$$

and

$$5s\bar{\imath}_2-5i_2(0)+200\bar{\imath}_2+3s\bar{\imath}_1-3i_1(0) = 0 \tag{6}$$

Now when $t = 0$, $\quad i_1(0) = i_2(0) = 0$

$\therefore$ substitution in equations (5) and (6)

$$\therefore\ \bar{\imath}_1(5s+200)+\bar{\imath}_2\,.\,3s = \frac{200}{s} \tag{7}$$

and

$$\bar{\imath}_2(5s+200)+\bar{\imath}_1\,.\,3s = 0 \tag{8}$$

Multiply equation (7) by $3s$ and equation (8) by $(5s+200)$

$$\therefore\ \bar{\imath}_1\,.\,3s(5s+200)+\bar{\imath}_2\,.\,9s^2 = 600 \tag{9}$$

and

$$\bar{\imath}_1\,.\,3s(5s+200)+\bar{\imath}_2(5s+200)(5s+200) = 0 \tag{10}$$

Subtracting equation (9) from equation (10)

$$\bar{i}_2(16s^2+2000s+40{,}000) = -600$$

$$\bar{i}_2(s^2+125s+2500) = -\frac{600}{16}$$

$$\therefore\ \bar{i}_2 = -\frac{75}{2}\cdot\frac{1}{(s+25)(s+100)}$$

$$= -\frac{75}{2}\cdot\frac{1}{75}\cdot\frac{100-25}{(s+25)(s+100)}$$

From the tables of Laplace transforms,

$$\therefore\ i_2 = -\tfrac{1}{2}(\varepsilon^{-25t}-\varepsilon^{-100t})$$

$$= \underline{\tfrac{1}{2}(\varepsilon^{-100t}-\varepsilon^{-25t})\ \text{A}}\quad \textit{Ans.}$$

Multiply equation (3) by 3 and equation (4) by 5,

$$\therefore\ 15\frac{di_1}{dt}+600i_1+9\frac{di_2}{dt} = 600 \qquad (11)$$

and

$$15\frac{di_1}{dt}+1000i_2+25\frac{di_2}{dt} = 0 \qquad (12)$$

Subtract equation (11) from equation (12),

$$16\frac{di_2}{dt}+1000i_2-600i_1 = -600$$

$$\therefore\ i_1 = \frac{2}{75}\frac{di_2}{dt}+\frac{5}{3}i_2+1$$

Hence, from the equation for i_2,

$$\frac{2}{75}\cdot\frac{di_2}{dt} = \frac{1}{75}(-100\varepsilon^{-100t}+25\varepsilon^{-25t})$$

$$\frac{5}{3}i_2 = \frac{5}{6}(\varepsilon^{-100t}-\varepsilon^{-25t})$$

$$1 = 1$$

Add

$$i_1 = -\tfrac{1}{2}\varepsilon^{-100t}-\tfrac{1}{2}\varepsilon^{-25t}+1$$

$$= \underline{1-\tfrac{1}{2}(\varepsilon^{-100t}+\varepsilon^{-25t})\ \text{A}}\quad \textit{Ans.}$$

In order to find the time at which the secondary current i_2 reaches its maximum value, equate di_2/dt to zero.

$$\therefore \frac{di_2}{dt} = -50\varepsilon^{-100t} + \frac{25}{2}\varepsilon^{-25t} = 0$$

$$\therefore 2\varepsilon^{-100t} = \tfrac{1}{2}\varepsilon^{-25t}$$

$$4 = \varepsilon^{75t}$$

$$\therefore t = \frac{1}{75}\ln 4 = \frac{1}{75}.1{\cdot}386$$

$$= \underline{18{\cdot}5 \text{ ms}} \quad \textit{Ans.}$$

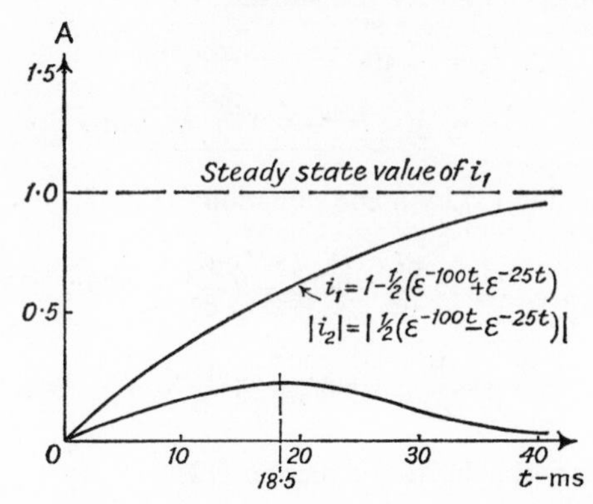

Fig. 9.7.—Sketch of primary current and the magnitude of the secondary current

3. Explain what is meant by amplitude modulation.

The output current i and input voltage v of a device are related by the expression $i = av + bv^2$. If sinusoidal signal and carrier voltages are applied in series to such a device, show that amplitude modulation is produced. Show also that the depth of modulation produced is, in general, not equal to the signal/carrier voltage-ratio.

If the values of a and b are, respectively 1·5 and 0·02, calculate the signal voltage to produce 10% modulation of a carrier of 5 V peak. What frequencies will be present in the output if the carrier frequency is 1 kc/s and the signal frequency is 50 c/s?

Solution For the explanation of amplitude modulation see Paper No. IV—June 1961, question No. 6, page 59.

Using the same symbols as in the previous question quoted above let

$$v = (\hat{V}_c \sin \omega_c t + \hat{V}_m \sin \omega_m t)$$

Now

$$i = av + bv^2$$

$$= a(\hat{V}_c \sin \omega_c t + \hat{V}_m \sin \omega_m t) + b(\hat{V}_c \sin \omega_c t + \hat{V}_m \sin \omega_m t)^2$$

$$= a\hat{V}_c \sin \omega_c t + a\hat{V}_m \sin \omega_m t + b\hat{V}_c^{\,2} \sin^2 \omega_c t + b\hat{V}_m^{\,2} \sin^2 \omega_m t$$
$$+ 2b\hat{V}_c\hat{V}_m \sin \omega_c t . \sin \omega_m t$$

$$= a\hat{V}_c \sin \omega_c t + a\hat{V}_m \sin \omega_m t + \frac{b}{2}\hat{V}_c^{\,2} - \frac{b}{2}\hat{V}_c^{\,2} \cos 2\,\omega_c t$$
$$+ \frac{b}{2}\hat{V}_m^{\,2} - \frac{b}{2}\hat{V}_m^{\,2} \cos 2\omega_m t + bV_cV_m \cos(\omega_c - \omega_m)t$$
$$- b\hat{V}_c\hat{V}_m \cos(\omega_c + \omega_m)t$$

$= \frac{b}{2}\hat{V}_c^{\,2} + \frac{b}{2}\hat{V}_m^{\,2}$ d.c. term

$+ a\hat{V}_c \sin \omega_c t$ the carrier

$+ a\hat{V}_m \sin \omega_m t$ the modulating signal

$- \frac{b}{2}\hat{V}_c^{\,2} \cos 2\,\omega_c t$ second harmonic of the carrier

$- \frac{b}{2}\hat{V}_m^{\,2} \cos 2\,\omega_m t$ second harmonic of the modulating signal

$+ b\hat{V}_c\hat{V}_m \cos(\omega_c - \omega_m)t$ the lower side band (L.S.B.)

$- b\hat{V}_c\hat{V}_m \cos(\omega_c + \omega_m)t$ the upper side band (U.S.B.)

This non-linear device produces the carrier, the L.S.B., and the U.S.B. This process shows that amplitude modulation has been achieved.

The depth of modulation of the resulting current

$= \frac{2 \times I_{SB}}{I_c} = m_a$ with the same definitions as on page 61

$= \frac{2 \times b\hat{V}_c\hat{V}_m}{a\hat{V}_c} = 2\frac{b}{a}\hat{V}_m$ which is not equal to $\frac{\hat{V}_m}{\hat{V}_c}$ Q.E.D.

Given $a = 1{\cdot}5$, $b = 0{\cdot}02$, $m_a = 10\% = \frac{1}{10}$

$$\therefore\; m_a = \frac{1}{10} = \frac{2 \times 0{\cdot}02}{1{\cdot}5}\hat{V}_m$$

$\therefore$ The peak value of the signal voltage $= \hat{V}_m = \underline{3{\cdot}75 \text{ V}}$ *Ans.*

If $f_c = 1$ kc/s and $f_m = 50$ c/s, by inspection of the expression for i above the following frequencies will be present in the output,

1. The carrier $a\hat{V}_c \sin \omega_c t$, giving a frequency component of 1 kc/s.

2. The modulating signal, $a\hat{V}_m \sin \omega_m t$, giving a frequency component of 50 c/s.

3. The second harmonic of the carrier, $-(b/2)\hat{V}_c^2 \cos 2\omega_c t$, giving a frequency component of 2 kc/s.

4. The second harmonic of the modulating signal, $-(b/2)\hat{V}_m^2 \cos 2\omega_m t$, giving a frequency component of 100 c/s.

5. The lower side band, $b\hat{V}_c\hat{V}_m \cos(\omega_c - \omega_m)t$, giving a frequency component of $(1000-50) = 950$ c/s.

6. The upper side band $b\hat{V}_c\hat{V}_m \cos(\omega_c + \omega_m)t$, giving a frequency component of $(1000+50) = 1050$ c/s.

4. Derive an expression for the current at any point along a uniform transmission line in terms of the sending-end voltage and current, the characteristic impedance Z_0, the propagation coefficient γ of the line, and the distance x from the sending end of the line.

At a certain frequency a 20-mile length of line has a characteristic impedance of $600\underline{/0^\circ}$ Ω. The attenuation coefficient is 0·1 neper/mile and the phase-change coefficient is 0·05 rad/mile. If the sending-end current is $0{\cdot}02\underline{/-30^\circ}$ A when a voltage of 15 V is applied to the line, determine the magnitude and phase angle of the current at the distant end.

Solution

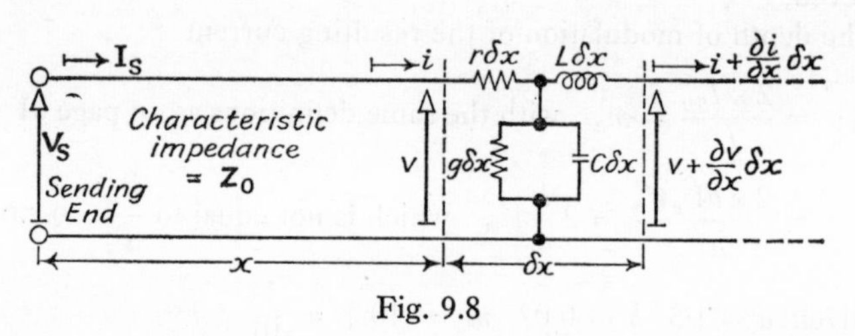

Fig. 9.8

Consider an elemental section, of the uniform transmission, of length δx, distant x units from the sending end. Let the instantaneous value of the voltage applied to the elemental section be v, and the instantaneous value of the current flowing into the elemental section be i. The instantaneous value of the voltage and current on the other side of the section are as shown in Fig. 9.8. The partial derivatives being used since both v and i are varying with respect to time as well as distance.

For the uniform transmission line let:

r = the resistance per unit length in Ω
L = the inductance per unit length in H
C = the capacitance per unit length in F
g = the leakage per unit length in mho

Assuming that the current is constant through the elemental section, the voltage equation is given by

$$v-\left(v+\frac{\partial v}{\partial x}\,\delta x\right) = r\,\delta x\,i+I\,\delta x\,\frac{\partial i}{\partial t} \tag{1}$$

Assuming that the voltage across the elemental section is constant, the current equation is given by

$$i-\left(i+\frac{\partial i}{\partial x}\,\delta x\right) = g\,\delta x\,v+C\,\delta x\,\frac{\partial v}{\partial t} \tag{2}$$

From equations (1) and (2),

$$-\frac{\partial v}{\partial x} = r\,i+L\,\frac{\partial i}{\partial t} \tag{3}$$

$$-\frac{\partial i}{\partial x} = g\,v+C\,\frac{\partial v}{\partial t} \tag{4}$$

Assuming that the sending-end voltage and current are sinusoidal and continue as sine waves down the line, we may write

$$v = \mathbf{V}\,\varepsilon^{j\omega t} \tag{5}$$

and

$$i = \mathbf{I}\,\varepsilon^{j\omega t} \tag{6}$$

where V and I are the r.m.s. value of the voltage and current at a distance x from the sending end of the transmission line.

Substituting equations (5) and (6) in equations (3) and (4)

$$-\frac{d\mathbf{V}}{dx}\,\varepsilon^{j\omega t} = \mathbf{I}\,\varepsilon^{j\omega t}(r+j\omega L) \tag{7}$$

and

$$-\frac{d\mathbf{I}}{dx}\,\varepsilon^{j\omega t} = \mathbf{V}\,\varepsilon^{j\omega t}(g+j\omega C) \tag{8}$$

the partial derivatives now being replaced by ordinary derivatives since the relation between voltage and current and time has been introduced.

From equations (7) and (8)

$$-\frac{dV}{dx} = I(r+j\omega L) \tag{9}$$

and

$$-\frac{dI}{dx} = V(g+j\omega C) \tag{10}$$

Differentiating equations (9) and (10) with respect to x,

$$-\frac{d^2V}{dx^2} = \frac{dI}{dx}(r+j\omega L)$$

$$= -(r+j\omega L)(g+j\omega C).V \tag{11}$$

and

$$-\frac{d^2I}{dx^2} = \frac{dV}{dx}(g+j\omega C)$$

$$= -(r+j\omega L)(g+j\omega C).I \tag{12}$$

Now $\sqrt{(r+j\omega L)(g+j\omega C)}$ is constant for a particular line, and is called the propagation coefficient γ. Hence, from equations (12) and (13),

$$\frac{d^2V}{dx^2} = \gamma^2.V \tag{13}$$

and

$$\frac{d^2I}{dx^2} = \gamma^2.I \tag{14}$$

The solution of equations (13) and (14) are

$$V = A\,\varepsilon^{\gamma x} + B\,\varepsilon^{-\gamma x} \tag{15}$$

and

$$I = C\,\varepsilon^{\gamma x} + D\,\varepsilon^{-\gamma x} \tag{16}$$

Since the voltage **V** and the current **I** are dependent quantities there is a relationship between the constants **A**, **B** and **C**, **D**.

From equations (15) and (9),

$$\frac{dV}{dx} = \gamma A\,\varepsilon^{\gamma x} - \gamma B\,\varepsilon^{-\gamma x}$$

$$= -I(r+j\omega L)$$

$$\therefore\ I = -\frac{\gamma}{(r+j\omega L)}A\,\varepsilon^{\gamma x} + \frac{\gamma}{(r+j\omega L)}B\,\varepsilon^{-\gamma x} \tag{17}$$

Now $\frac{\gamma}{(r+j\omega L)} = \sqrt{\frac{(g+j\omega C)}{(r+j\omega L)}}$ and has the dimensions of mho; thus $\sqrt{\frac{(r+j\omega L)}{(g+j\omega C)}}$ has the dimensions of ohm and is called the characteristic impedance Z_0.

$\therefore$ from equation (17),

$$\mathbf{I} = -\frac{\mathbf{A}}{\mathbf{Z}_0}\cdot\varepsilon^{\gamma x}+\frac{\mathbf{B}}{\mathbf{Z}_0}\cdot\varepsilon^{-\gamma x} \tag{18}$$

Let $\mathbf{A} = (\mathbf{H}+\mathbf{K})/2$ and $\mathbf{B} = (\mathbf{H}-\mathbf{K})/2$. Then substituting in equations (15) and (18),

$$\mathbf{V} = \mathbf{H}\left(\frac{\varepsilon^{\gamma x}+\varepsilon^{-\gamma x}}{2}\right)+\mathbf{K}\left(\frac{\varepsilon^{\gamma x}-\varepsilon^{-\gamma x}}{2}\right)$$

$$= \mathbf{H}\cosh\gamma x+\mathbf{K}\sinh\gamma x \tag{19}$$

and

$$\mathbf{I} = -\frac{\mathbf{K}}{\mathbf{Z}_0}\left(\frac{\varepsilon^{\gamma x}+\varepsilon^{-\gamma x}}{2}\right)-\frac{\mathbf{H}}{\mathbf{Z}_0}\left(\frac{\varepsilon^{\gamma x}-\varepsilon^{-\gamma x}}{2}\right)$$

$$= -\frac{\mathbf{K}}{\mathbf{Z}_0}\cosh\gamma x-\frac{\mathbf{H}}{\mathbf{Z}_0}\sinh\gamma x \tag{20}$$

Now when $x = 0$, $\mathbf{V} = \mathbf{V_S}$ and $\mathbf{I} = \mathbf{I_S}$

$\therefore$ from equation (19), $\mathbf{H} = \mathbf{V_S}$

and from equation (20), $-\dfrac{\mathbf{K}}{\mathbf{Z}_0} = \mathbf{I_S}$

$\therefore$ from equations (19) and (20),

$$\underline{\mathbf{V} = \mathbf{V_S}\cosh\gamma x-\mathbf{I_S}\mathbf{Z}_0\sinh\gamma x}$$

and

$$\underline{\mathbf{I} = \mathbf{I_S}\cosh\gamma x-\frac{\mathbf{V_S}}{\mathbf{Z}_0}\sinh\gamma x} \quad \textit{Ans.}$$

Note: although the question only asks for the current equation, the derivation does involve finding the voltage equation.

Given: $\mathbf{Z}_0 = 600\angle 0^\circ = 600(1+j0)\ \Omega$

$$\gamma = \alpha+j\beta = (0{\cdot}1+j0{\cdot}05)/\text{mile}$$

$$\mathbf{V_S} = 15\text{ V} = 15(1+j0) \quad \text{the reference vector}$$

$$\mathbf{I_S} = 0{\cdot}02\angle -30^\circ = 0{\cdot}02\left(\frac{\sqrt{3}}{2}-j\frac{1}{2}\right)\text{ A}$$

$$= 0{\cdot}01(\sqrt{3}-j)\text{ A}$$

$$x = 20\text{ mile}$$

$\therefore$ The current at the distant end

$$= \mathbf{I} = 0{\cdot}01(\sqrt{3}-j)\cosh(0{\cdot}1+j0{\cdot}05).20$$
$$-\frac{15}{600}\sinh(0{\cdot}1+j0{\cdot}05).20$$

$$= 0{\cdot}01(\sqrt{3}-j)\cosh(2+j1)-\frac{1}{40}\sinh(2+j1) \qquad (21)$$

Now $\cosh(2+j1) = \cosh 2 \cos 1 + j \sinh 2 \sin 1$

$$= (3{\cdot}762\times 0{\cdot}54)+j(3{\cdot}627\times 0{\cdot}842)$$
$$= (2{\cdot}03+j3{\cdot}05)$$

Also $\sinh(2+j1) = \sinh 2 \cos 1 + \mathrm{j} \cosh 2 . \sin 1$

$$= (3{\cdot}627\times 0{\cdot}54)+j(3{\cdot}762\times 0{\cdot}842)$$
$$= (1{\cdot}959+j3{\cdot}168)$$

$$\therefore \mathbf{I} = 0{\cdot}01(\sqrt{3}-j)(2{\cdot}03+j3{\cdot}05)-0{\cdot}025(1{\cdot}959+j3{\cdot}168)$$
$$= 0{\cdot}0657+j0{\cdot}0325-0{\cdot}049-j0{\cdot}0792$$
$$= (16{\cdot}7-j46{\cdot}7)\ \text{mA}$$
$$= \underline{49{\cdot}61\angle -70^\circ{\cdot}19'\ \text{mA with respect to } \mathbf{V_s}} \quad \textit{Ans.}$$

5. The speed of a flywheel, driven by an electric motor, is to be controlled from the setting of an input potentiometer using a closed-loop automatic speed-control system. Draw a labelled block diagram for such a system, and set up a differential equation for it assuming that there is viscous friction. Time lags in the motor and control equipment may be neglected.

The inclusive moment of inertia of the flywheel and motor is 100 kg-m^2 and a speed error of 1 rad/s produces a torque on the flywheel of 45 Nm. The frictional torque is 5 Nm when the flywheel velocity is 1 rad/s. With the system at rest the input potentiometer setting is suddenly increased from zero to 100 rev/min. Derive the relation between the subsequent flywheel velocity and time, and calculate the steady-state velocity error of the flywheel.

Solution For the labelled block diagram of the closed-loop automatic speed-control system see Paper No. III—November, 1960, question No. 6, page 44. For definitions of the terms and proof of the differential equation see Paper No. IV—June 1961, question No. 7, page 61.

In this example θ_o and θ_i are both functions of t, and the definition of K is the torque in Nm/rad/s of speed error between the input and output shafts.

∴ The equation of motion is

$$J\frac{d^2\theta_o}{dt^2}+F\frac{d\theta_o}{dt} = K\left(\frac{d\theta_i}{dt}-\frac{d\theta_o}{dt}\right) = \left\{\begin{matrix}\text{the torque due to the}\\ \text{velocity error}\end{matrix}\right.$$

$$\therefore\; J\frac{d^2\theta_o}{dt^2}+F\frac{d\theta_o}{dt}+K\frac{d\theta_o}{dt} = K\frac{d\theta_i}{dt}$$

Given: $J = 100$ kg-m^2

$F = 5$ Nm/rad/s

$K = 45$ Nm/rad/s

$$\frac{d\theta_i}{dt} = 100\text{ rev/min} = \frac{100}{60}\times 2\pi\text{ rad/s}$$

$$\therefore\; 100\frac{d^2\theta_o}{dt^2}+5\frac{d\theta_o}{dt}+45\frac{d\theta_o}{dt} = 45\times\frac{100}{60}\times 2\pi$$

$$\therefore\; \frac{d^2\theta_o}{dt^2}+\frac{1}{2}\frac{d\theta_o}{dt} = \frac{3\pi}{2}$$

Since the system is initially at rest the Laplace operator p may be used.

$$\therefore\; p^2\bar{\theta}_o+\tfrac{1}{2}p\bar{\theta}_o = \frac{3\pi}{2}\cdot\frac{1}{p}$$

since the input is a step function of velocity.

$$\therefore\; \bar{\theta}_o\cdot p(p+\tfrac{1}{2}) = \frac{3\pi}{2}\cdot\frac{1}{p}$$

$$\therefore\; \bar{\theta}_o = \frac{3\pi}{2}\cdot\frac{1}{p^2(p+\frac{1}{2})}$$

$$= \frac{3\pi}{2}\cdot(-2)\cdot\frac{p-(p+\frac{1}{2})}{p^2(p+\frac{1}{2})}$$

$$= \frac{3\pi}{2}\cdot(-2)\left[2\cdot\frac{\frac{1}{2}}{p(p+\frac{1}{2})}-\frac{1}{p^2}\right]$$

Using the tables of Laplace transforms,

$$\therefore\; \theta_o = [-6\pi(1-\varepsilon^{-t/2})+3\pi t]\text{ rad}$$

∴ The relationship between the subsequent flywheel velocity and time is

$$\frac{d\theta_o}{dt} = -3\pi\,\varepsilon^{-t/2} + 3\pi$$

$$= 3\pi(1-\varepsilon^{-t/2}) \text{ rad/s} \quad \textit{Ans.}$$

Under steady-state conditions, i.e. as $t \to \infty$

$$\frac{d\theta_o}{dt} = 3\pi \text{ rad/s}$$

$$\text{Input velocity} = \frac{d\theta i}{dt} = \frac{10\pi}{3} \text{ rad/s}$$

∴ Steady-state velocity error of the flywheel

$$= \frac{d\theta_i}{dt} - \frac{d\theta_o}{dt} = \frac{10\pi}{3} - 3\pi$$

$$= \frac{\pi}{3} \text{ rad/s}$$

$$= \frac{\pi}{3} \times 60 \times \frac{1}{2\pi} \text{ rev/min.}$$

$$= 10 \text{ rev/min} \quad \textit{Ans.}$$

6. In Fig. 9.9, three non-reactive resistors $R_1 = 10\ \Omega$, $R_2 = 20\ \Omega$, and $R_3 = 30\ \Omega$, are connected in star to a symmetrical 3-phase supply of line voltage 400 V and phase-sequence RYB. The wattmeter W is connected, as shown, with the current coil in the R line and the voltage circuit connected between lines R and Y. Calculate the current in the three lines and the reading of the wattmeter.

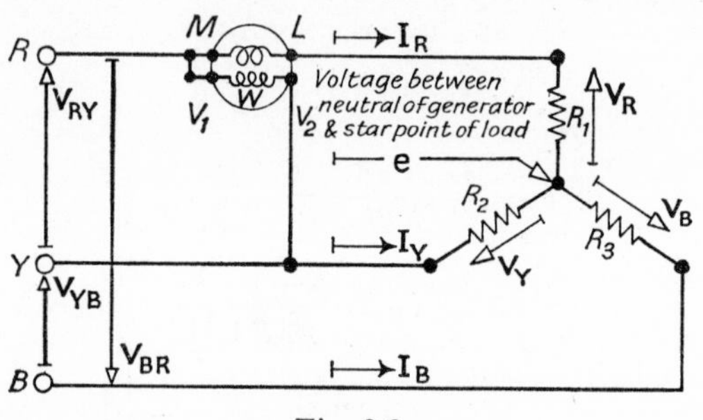

Fig. 9.9

Note: the conventional directions of voltage and current, the wattmeter current and voltage coils, and the symbols used on the wattmeter, were not indicated in the original question.

Solution 1. Using the conventional directions of voltage and current as indicated in the figure.

2. Using a phase sequence of RYB.

3. Choosing the Red phase balanced generator voltage as a reference vector, i.e.

$$\mathbf{E_R} = E(1+j0)$$

$$\therefore\ \mathbf{E_Y} = a^2E$$

and

$$\mathbf{E_B} = aE$$

4. Assume that if current flows from M to L, and $V_1 > V_2$ the wattmeter W will read positive.

Now by inspection of Fig. 9.9,

$$\mathbf{I_R} = \frac{\mathbf{V_R}}{R_1} = \frac{\mathbf{E_R}-\mathbf{e}}{10} = \frac{E-\mathbf{e}}{10}\ \text{A} \tag{1}$$

$$\mathbf{I_Y} = \frac{\mathbf{V_Y}}{R_2} = \frac{\mathbf{E_Y}-\mathbf{e}}{20} = \frac{a^2E-\mathbf{e}}{20}\ \text{A} \tag{2}$$

$$\mathbf{I_B} = \frac{\mathbf{V_B}}{R_3} = \frac{\mathbf{E_B}-\mathbf{e}}{30} = \frac{aE-\mathbf{e}}{30}\ \text{A} \tag{3}$$

Also, since the system is 3-phase, 3-wire,

$$\mathbf{I_R}+\mathbf{I_Y}+\mathbf{I_B} = 0 \tag{4}$$

$\therefore$ Substituting equations (1), (2), and (3) in equation (4),

$$\frac{E-\mathbf{e}}{10}+\frac{a^2E-\mathbf{e}}{20}+\frac{aE-\mathbf{e}}{30} = 0$$

$$\therefore\ \mathbf{e} = \frac{E(3a^2+2a+6)}{11}$$

$$= \frac{E(a^2+4)}{11} \quad \text{since } 2(1+a+a^2) = 0$$

From equation (1),

$$\mathbf{I_R} = E\frac{1-\dfrac{(a^2+4)}{11}}{10}$$

$$= E\frac{(7-a^2)}{110}$$

$$= \frac{400}{\sqrt{3}}\cdot\frac{1}{110}\cdot\frac{1}{2}(15+j\sqrt{3})\ \text{A} \quad \text{since } a^2 = -\tfrac{1}{2}-j\frac{\sqrt{3}}{2}$$

$$= \underline{15{\cdot}85\angle 6^\circ{\cdot}36'\ \text{A} \quad \text{with respect to } \mathbf{E_R}} \quad \textit{Ans.}$$

From equation (2),

$$\mathbf{I_Y} = E\frac{a^2-\dfrac{(a^2+4)}{11}}{20}$$

$$= E\frac{10a^2-4}{20\times 11}$$

$$= \frac{E}{220}\cdot(-9-j5\sqrt{3})$$

$$= \frac{400}{\sqrt{3}}\cdot\frac{1}{220}\cdot(-9-j5\sqrt{3})$$

$$= \underline{13{\cdot}1\angle 223^\circ{\cdot}54' \text{ A} \quad \text{with respect to } E_R} \quad \textit{Ans.}$$

From equation (3),

$$\mathbf{I_B} = E\frac{a-\dfrac{(a^2+4)}{11}}{30}$$

$$= E\frac{(11a-a^2-4)}{30\times 11}$$

$$= E\frac{(12a-3)}{330} \quad \text{since } a^2+a+1 = 0$$

$$= \frac{E}{110}\cdot(-3+j2\sqrt{3}) \quad \text{since } a = -\tfrac{1}{2}+j\frac{\sqrt{3}}{2}$$

$$= \frac{400}{\sqrt{3}}\cdot\frac{1}{110}\cdot(-3+j2\sqrt{3})$$

$$= \underline{9{\cdot}63\angle 130^\circ{\cdot}54' \text{ A} \quad \text{with respect to } E_R} \quad \textit{Ans.}$$

The wattmeter W reads the dot product of

$$\mathbf{V_{RY}}.\mathbf{I_R}$$

$$= \text{dot product of } E(1-a^2)\cdot\frac{400}{\sqrt{3}}\cdot\frac{1}{110}\cdot\frac{1}{2}(15+j\sqrt{3})$$

$$= \text{dot product of } \frac{400}{\sqrt{3}}\cdot\frac{400}{\sqrt{3}}\cdot\frac{1}{110}\cdot\frac{1}{2}\cdot\frac{1}{2}(3+j\sqrt{3})(15+j\sqrt{3})$$

$$= \frac{4\times 4}{3\times 11\times 4}\cdot(45+3) \text{ kW}$$

$$= \underline{5{\cdot}82 \text{ kW}} \quad \textit{Ans.}$$

PAPER NO. X—Unworked Classified Examples

1. State the conditions that must be fulfilled if a load impedance is to extract the maximum possible power from a source of e.m.f. E volts and internal impedance $(R+jX)$ Ω.

A four-terminal π-network has a series arm of impedance $(5+j12)$ Ω, and each shunt arm consists of a capacitor of reactance 5 Ω. The network is connected to a generator of 100 V, and internal impedance $(5+j12)$ Ω. Find the components of the load impedance to be connected across two terminals of the four-terminal network in order to dissipate maximum power in the load, and evaluate this power. State also the conditions to be fulfilled in order to dissipate maximum power in the generator, and evaluate this power (H.N.D.)

(*Ans.* The load impedance for the dissipation of maximum power is $(3{\cdot}73+j4{\cdot}8)$ Ω. The maximum power dissipated in this load is 126 W. The condition for maximum power in the generator is that the generator load is $-j12$ Ω, and the corresponding generator power is 2 kW.)

2. Find the magnitude and phase angle of the current in the load connected to the terminals A and B of the network shown in Fig. 10.1 by means of the continuous application of Thévenin's Theorem. Hence find the power dissipated in the load. (H.N.D.)

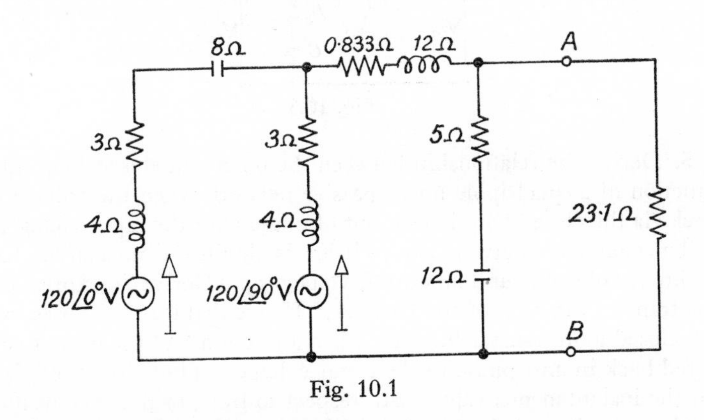

Fig. 10.1

(*Ans.* $6{\cdot}44\backslash\underline{22{\cdot}4^\circ}$ A; 965 W).

3. The circuit shown below in Fig. 10.2 has a mutual inductance coupling of 90 μH. Find (*a*) the input impedance of the circuit at its resonant frequency, and (*b*) the gain of the network in db, at its resonant frequency. (H.N.D.)

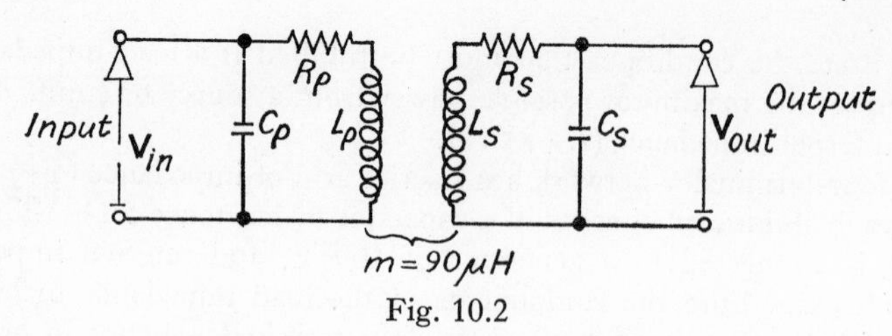

Fig. 10.2

$$C_p = 800\ \mu\mu F,\quad L_p = 500\ \mu H,\quad R_p = 30\ \Omega$$

$$C_s = 500\ \mu\mu F,\quad L_s = 800\ \mu H,\quad R_s = 40\ \Omega$$

(*Ans.* (*a*) $(1170 - j780)\ \Omega$; (*b*) 13·5 db.)

4. Show, algebraically, and by means of a vector diagram that the network shown in Fig. 10.3 acts as a phase lag network, i.e. $\mathbf{V}_{out}$ lags $\mathbf{V}_{in}$ for all values of frequency greater than zero. Express $\mathbf{V}_{out}/\mathbf{V}_{in}$ in the form $(1+pT\alpha)/(1+pT)$ where $\alpha = R_2/(R_1+R_2)$ and $p = j\omega$, and deduce an expression for the maximum value of the phase shift in the form $\phi_{max} = \sin^{-1}\{(1-\alpha)/(1+\alpha)\}$, assuming the frequency is varied.

State briefly a suitable use for this type of network. (H.N.D.)

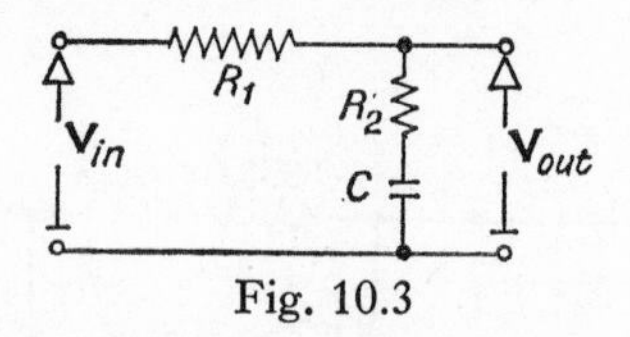

Fig. 10.3

5. Derive the relationship between the open and closed-loop transfer function of a quadripole linear passive network when the voltage feedback via the closed loop is 180° out of phase with the input voltage.

The equivalent network shown below is obtained from a circuit having an input voltage v_i and an output voltage v_o. Derive an expression for the transfer function of the network. Hence deduce the expression for the closed loop transfer function when a fraction k of the output voltage is fed back in anti-phase to the input voltage. Find also an expression for the instantaneous value, with respect to time, of the current flowing in the capacitor C due to the rising edge of a pulse of amplitude v_i applied at the input under closed loop conditions. (A.M-E.C.)

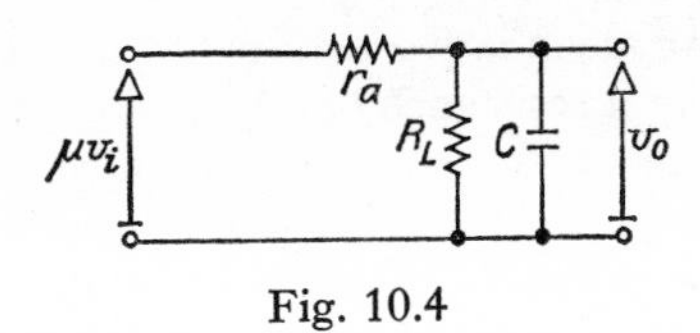

Fig. 10.4

(*Ans.* Transfer function $= \dfrac{\dfrac{\mu}{r_a C}}{p+\dfrac{r_a+R_L}{r_a R_L C}}$

Closed loop transfer function $= \dfrac{\dfrac{\mu}{r_a C}}{p+\dfrac{r_a+R_L(1+\mu k)}{r_a R_L C}}$

Capacitor current $= \dfrac{\mu v_i}{r_a}\,\varepsilon^{\frac{-r_a+R_L(1+\mu k)}{r_a R_L C}\cdot t}$.)

6. Define the term 'transfer function' when referring to a quadripole network containing linear passive bilateral elements. Hence derive an expression for the transfer function of a number of dissimilar quadripole networks when connected in tandem, and state the conditions that must hold for the derived expression to be true.

The two networks shown in Fig. 10.5 are joined by an ideal cathode follower. The resistors *R* and the capacitors *C* have the same value in both networks. Derive an expression for the overall transfer function of the combined networks. Hence find the output voltage/time domain relationship if the input voltage is of the form $t\,\varepsilon^{-t/CR}$. (A.M-E.C.)

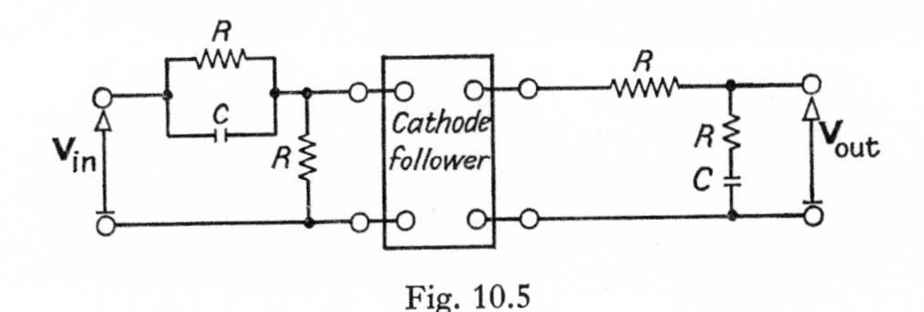

Fig. 10.5

(*Ans.* The overall transfer function $= \dfrac{\left(p+\dfrac{1}{RC}\right)^2}{2\left(p+\dfrac{2}{RC}\right)\left(p+\dfrac{1}{2RC}\right)}$

where $p = j\omega$.

The output voltage $= -\ 17{\cdot}866\ \varepsilon^{-t/2RC}$ volts.)

7. The primary and secondary windings of a transformer each have an inductance of 1 H and a resistance of 40 Ω, and the mutual inductance between the windings is 0·6 H. The secondary winding is short-circuited and the primary winding is suddenly connected to a 40 V d.c. supply of negligible impedance. Derive expressions for the primary and secondary currents and calculate the time at which the secondary current has its maximum value. (A.E.E., November,1958)

(*Ans.* The secondary current $= 0{\cdot}5(\varepsilon^{-100t} - \varepsilon^{-25t})$ A.
The primary current $= 1 + \frac{1}{6}(27\varepsilon^{-100t} - \varepsilon^{-25t})$ A.
The time at which the secondary current has its maximum value is 18·5 ms.)

8. Define the following terms with reference to quadripole networks containing linear passive bilateral elements: (*a*) Iterative impedance, (*b*) Image impedance, (*c*) Insertion loss.

Find the image impedances of the network shown in Fig. 10.6. Hence find the insertion loss of the network when it is inserted between its image impedances. (A.M-E.C.)

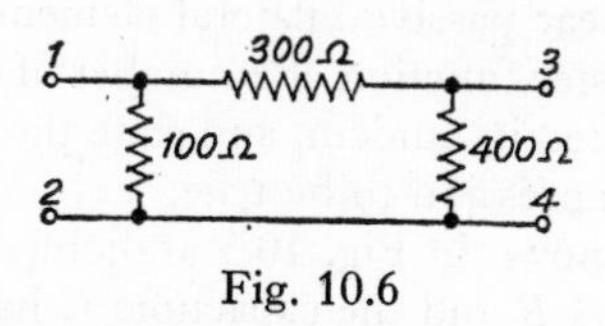

Fig. 10.6

(*Ans.* The image impedance to be placed across terminals 1–2 is 79·25 Ω.
The image impedance to be placed across terminals 3–4 is 185·2 Ω.
The insertion loss is 13·4 db.)

9. Derive the values of the characteristic impedance and propagation constant of the network in Fig. 10.7. (A.M-E.C.)

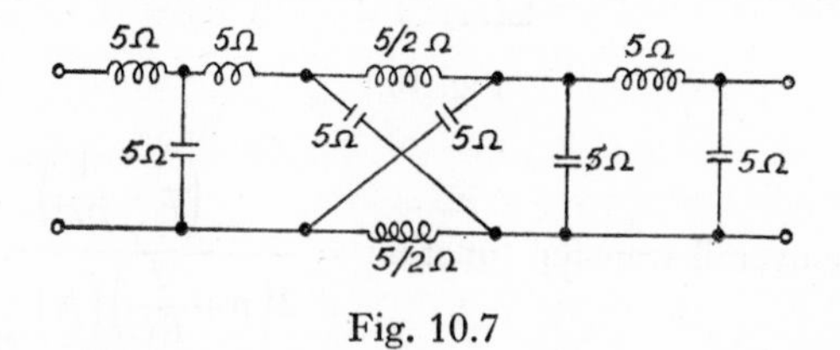

Fig. 10.7

(*Note*: this problem is most readily solved by means of matrix algebra e.g. find the **A, B, C, D** constants and use the equations $\mathbf{Z}_0 = \sqrt{\mathbf{B}/\mathbf{C}}$ and $\varepsilon^{\gamma} = \mathbf{C}\mathbf{Z}_0 + \mathbf{D}$.)

(*Ans.* $\mathbf{Z}_0$ is an inductance of reactance 1 Ω.
$\gamma = \ln 2{\cdot}4 - j\pi/2$.)

10. A single T-section constant k low pass filter is to be used as a matching device over a narrow band of frequencies. It is required to match a resistive impedance of 400 Ω to one of 625 Ω in the region of 1 Mc/s. Calculate the design impedance, and cut-off frequency of the filter, and hence determine the value of the passive elements of the filter. (A.M-E.C.)

(*Ans.* 707 Ω, 1·414 Mc/s.
Each series element of the T-section is an inductance of 79·5 μH.
The shunt element of the T-section is a capacitor of 318 pF.)

11. A single section constant k low pass filter has an inductance of 0·5 mH in each series arm and a shunt capacitance of 0·1 μF. A symmetrical square voltage wave of fundamental frequency 10 kc/s is applied to one end of the filter. The harmonic composition of this square wave is

$$V = 10(\sin \omega t + \tfrac{1}{3}\sin 3\omega t + \tfrac{1}{5}\sin 5\omega t + \tfrac{1}{7}\sin 7\omega t + \cdots)$$

The propagation constant γ of the filter is given by $\cosh\gamma = 1 + Z_1/2Z_2$. Sketch the resulting output waveform and state which harmonics of the input make an appreciable contribution to the output. (A.M-E.C.)

(*Ans.* The fundamental and the third harmonic component of frequency for which the phase shifts are 36·9° and 143·1° respectively.)

12. Show that a 3-phase system, having a line voltage V, and total power P and impedance per line Z, has the same regulation and efficiency as a single phase system with a voltage V, power P, and loop impedance Z.

A 3-phase 50 c/s transmission line 100 miles long has a conductor resistance of 0·25 Ω/mile, a line-to-neutral inductance of 2·55 mH/mile, a capacitance of 0·0446 μF/mile, and negligible leakance. Find the sending-end voltage when supplying a receiving-end load of 60 MVA at 275 kV and power factor 0·8 (lagging). Draw a vector diagram and derive any formulae used in the calculation. (A.E.E., June, 1959)

(*Ans.* 274 kV.)

13. Three equal impedance arms AB, BC, CA are connected in delta to the terminals A, B, C of a 3-phase supply. Each arm consists of two resistors and a capacitor connected in series in the order shown in Fig. 10.8. The relation between the ohmic values of the components is given by $R:r:1/\omega C = 2:1:\sqrt{3}$, and high-impedance voltmeters V_1, V_2, V_3 are connected to the network shown. If the supply-line voltages V_{AB}, V_{BC}, V_{CA} are balanced, determine *either* graphically *or* algebraically the readings of the three voltmeters.

(*a*) when the phase sequence of the supply is *A—B—C*,
and (*b*) when the phase sequence of the supply is reversed.

Hence explain how the network could be employed to measure respectively the positive phase-sequence and the negative phase-sequence voltage components of an asymmetrical 3-phase supply.

(A.E.E., November, 1958)

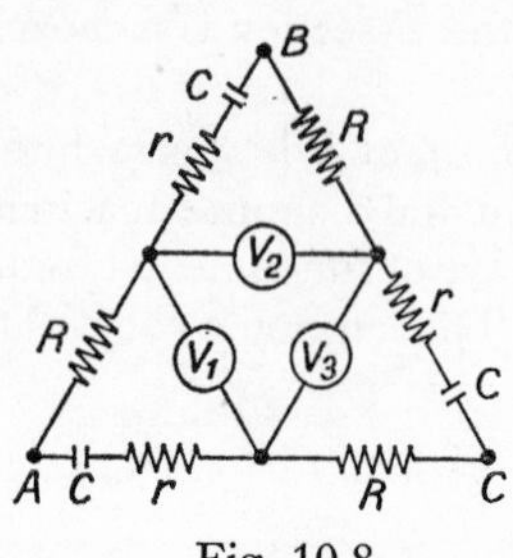

Fig. 10.8

(*Ans.* (*a*) Each of the three voltmeters will read the magnitude of the balanced line voltage.
(*b*) Each of the three voltmeters will read zero volts.)

14. Two star connected loads are supplied from a balanced 3-phase, 3-wire supply of 400 V. One star connected load consists of three non-inductive resistors each of resistance 20 Ω. The other star connected load has impedances $(1+j2)$ Ω in the Red phase, $(2+j4)$ Ω in the Yellow phase, and $(4+j8)$ Ω in the Blue phase. The phase sequence is *RYB*.

Calculate the voltage between the star points of the parallel loads, and the total supply line currents (H.N.D.)

(*Ans.* $87.4\overline{\backslash 19{\cdot}3^\circ}$ V: The Red line current $= 75\overline{\backslash 45{\cdot}4^\circ}$ A.
The Yellow line current $= 60{\cdot}2\underline{/168{\cdot}2^\circ}$ A.
The Blue line current $= 42{\cdot}6\underline{/80{\cdot}4^\circ}$ A.)

15. Four terminals *R*, *Y*, *B*, and *N* represent a balanced 400 V, 3-phase star-connected, 4-wire alternator of phase sequence *RYB*. The terminals *R* and *Y* are joined by an impedance *Z* of unknown value.

The current coils of two wattmeters are connected in the R and Y lines, and their respective voltage coils meet at the terminal N. The wattmeters in the R and Y lines read 25 kW and -6 kW respectively. Calculate:

(*a*) the current taken from the supply,
(*b*) the power factor of the load,
(*c*) the resistance and reactance of the unknown impedance Z.

(H.N.D.)

(*Ans.* (*a*) 142·4 A; (*b*) 0·33 lead; (*c*) Resistance of 0·936 Ω in series with a capacitance reactance of 2·65 Ω.)

16. In a three-phase, 50 c/s alternator of phase sequence RYB, the voltage of the Red phase is given by

$$E_R = E_1 \sin \omega t + E_3 \sin 3\omega t + E_5 \sin 5\omega t$$

Show that the fifth harmonics of the RYB phases have a negative phase sequence.

The generated e.m.f. per phase is approximately 506 V, with 12% third harmonic and 8% fifth harmonic. The resistance and inductance of each phase of the winding is 2·5 Ω and 10 mH respectively. Calculate:

(*a*) the r.m.s. line voltage for star and delta connection,
(*b*) the circulating current when delta connected,
(*c*) the current in a 50 μF capacitor connected across one phase when the alternator windings are connected in delta. (H.N.D.)

(*Ans.* (*a*) 869 V, 502 V; (*b*) 6·16 A; (*c*) 7·88 A.)

17. Define the term 'servo-mechanism', and distinguish between coulomb and viscous friction damping when referring to an error actuated closed loop servo-mechanism.

Explain with the aid of a phase-plane diagram, the resulting motion of an error-actuated control damping, with a step function input, and state the disadvantages of such a system. (A.M-E.C.)

18. Describe briefly, showing the essential elements in a diagram, stabilized error-actuated automatic control systems suitable for two of the following:

(*a*) the speed control of a d.c. motor;
(*b*) the temperature control of an electric furnace; and
(*c*) the positional control of a rotatable mass.

(A.E.E., November, 1961)

19. Draw a block diagram for an error-actuated automatic control system for the position-control of a rotatable mass, the system being stabilized by output velocity feed-back, and viscous friction damping. Describe the purpose of the essential elements, and deduce the equation of motion of the system.

A flywheel driven by an electric motor is automatically controlled by the movement of a handwheel. The inclusive moment of inertia of the flywheel is 100 kg-m^2, and the torque applied to it is 0·727 Nm/min. of misalignment between the flywheel, and the handwheel. The damping torques due to velocity feed-back, and viscous friction are 700 Nm/rad/s, and 100 Nm/rad/s respectively. The handwheel is suddenly turned through 30° when the system is at rest. Derive an expression for the subsequent angular position of the flywheel in relation to time, and sketch the form of the function. (A.M-E.C.)

(*Ans.* $\theta_o = \frac{\pi}{6}\left[1-\frac{5}{3}\varepsilon^{-4t}.\sin(3t+\alpha)\right]$ rad where $\alpha = \tan^{-1}\frac{3}{4}$.)

20. The integrator stage of an electronic analogue computer consists of an operational amplifier with negative feedback applied. Show that the performance equation for n input voltages is given by

$$v_o = -\frac{1}{pC}\sum_{i=1}^{n}\frac{v_1}{R_1}$$

where v_o is the output voltage of the stage, $v_1, v_2, \ldots, v_n$ are the input voltages, $R_1, R_2 \ldots R_n$ are the input resistances and C is the capacitor in the feedback path.

Explain simply the process of programming for an analogue computer, and build up a flow diagram for an equation of the type

$$a\frac{d^2x}{dt^2}+b\frac{dx}{dt}+cx = f(t)$$

where a, b, and c are constants. (A.M-E.C.)

APPENDIX I

TABLE OF LAPLACE TRANSFORMS

$\mathcal{L}[f(t)]$ is defined by $\int_0^\infty f(t)\, \varepsilon^{-st}, dt$ and is written as $F(s)$.

$f(t)$ from $t = 0$	$F(s) = \mathcal{L}[f(t)]$
$\frac{d}{dt} f(t)$	$sF(s) - f(0)$
$\frac{d^n}{dt^n} f(t)$	$s^n F(s) - s^{n-1} f(0) - s^{n-2} f'(0) \ldots - f^{(n-1)}(0)$
$\int_0^t f(t)\, dt$	$\frac{1}{s} F(s)$
$\varepsilon^{-\alpha t} f(t)$	$F(s+\alpha)$ {The shifting Theorem}
Unit impulse δ	I
Unit function 1 or $H(t)$	$\frac{1}{s}$
Delayed unit function	$\frac{\varepsilon^{-sT}}{s}$
Rectangular pulse	$\frac{1-\varepsilon^{-sT}}{s}$
Ramp function t	$\frac{1}{s^2}$
$t^{n-1}/(n-1)!$	$\frac{1}{s^n}$
$\frac{t^{n-1}}{(n-1)!} \varepsilon^{-\alpha t}$	$\frac{1}{(s+\alpha)^n}$
$\varepsilon^{-\alpha t}$	$\frac{1}{(s+\alpha)}$
$1-\varepsilon^{-\alpha t}$	$\frac{\alpha}{s(s+\alpha)}$

$f(t)$ from $t = 0$	$F(s) = \mathscr{L}[f(t)]$
$t\,\varepsilon^{-\alpha t}$	$\dfrac{1}{(s+\alpha)^2}$
$\varepsilon^{-\alpha t}-\varepsilon^{-\beta t}$	$\dfrac{\beta-\alpha}{(s+\alpha)(s+\beta)}$
$\sin \omega t$	$\dfrac{\omega}{s^2+\omega^2}$
$\cos \omega t$	$\dfrac{s}{s^2+\omega^2}$
$1-\cos \omega t$	$\dfrac{\omega^2}{s(s^2+\omega^2)}$
$\omega t \sin \omega t$	$\dfrac{2\omega^2 s}{(s^2+\omega^2)^2}$
$\sin \omega t-\omega t \cos \omega t$	$\dfrac{2\omega^3}{(s^2+\omega^2)^2}$
$\varepsilon^{-\alpha t} \sin \omega t$	$\dfrac{\omega}{(s+\alpha)^2+\omega^2}$
$\varepsilon^{-\alpha t} \cos \omega t$	$\dfrac{s+\alpha}{(s+\alpha)^2+\omega^2}$
$\varepsilon^{-\alpha t}(\cos \omega t-\dfrac{\alpha}{\omega} \sin \omega t)$	$\dfrac{s}{(s+\alpha)^2+\omega^2}$
$\sin(\omega t+\phi)$	$\dfrac{s \sin \phi+\omega \cos \phi}{s^2+\omega^2}$
$\varepsilon^{-\alpha t}+(\alpha/\omega) \sin \omega t-\cos \omega t$	$\dfrac{\alpha^2+\omega^2}{(s+\alpha)(s^2+\omega^2)}$
$\sinh \beta t$	$\dfrac{\beta}{s^2-\beta^2}$
$\cosh \beta t$	$\dfrac{s}{s^2-\beta^2}$

APPENDIX II

CLASSIFIED LIST OF REFERENCES

Electrical measurements

Principles of Electrical Measurements by H. Buckingham and E. M. Price. English Universities Press Ltd.

Electrical Measurements and Measuring Instruments by E. W. Golding. Sir Isaac Pitman & Sons Ltd.

A.C. Bridge Methods by B. Hague. Sir Isaac Pitman & Sons Ltd.

Fundamentals of Electrical Measurements by C. T. Baldwin. George G. Harrap & Co. Ltd.

Electronic Measurements by F. E. Terman and J. M. Pettit. McGraw-Hill Publishing Co. Ltd.

Telecommunications

The Royal Signals Handbook of Line Communications, Vol. I. H.M.S.O.

Radio Engineering by F. E. Terman. McGraw-Hill Publishing Co. Ltd.

The Services Textbook of Radio, Vol. 5: *Transmission and Propagation* by E. V. D. Glazier and H. R. L. Lamont. H.M.S.O.

Radio Engineers Handbook by F. E. Terman. McGraw-Hill Publishing Co. Ltd.

Electronics by P. Parker. Edward Arnold (Publishers) Ltd.

Short Wave Wireless Communications including Ultra-Short Waves by A. W. Ladner and C. R. Stoner. Chapman & Hall Ltd.

Electrical power

Principles of Electric Power Transmission by H. Waddicor. Chapman & Hall Ltd.

Higher Electrical Engineering by J. Shepherd, A. H. Morton, and L. F. Spence. Sir Isaac Pitman & Sons Ltd.

Electrical Engineering (General) by A. T. Dover and F. T. Chapman. Longmans, Green & Co. Ltd.

Electrical Technology by H. Cotton. Sir Isaac Pitman & Sons Ltd.

Servomechanisms

Servomechanisms by J. C. West. English Universities Press Ltd.

An Introduction to Servo Mechanics by F. L. Westwater and W. A. Waddell. English Universities Press Ltd.

Servomechanism Practice by W. R. Ahrendt and C. J. Savant. McGraw-Hill Publishing Co. Ltd.

General network theory

Electric Circuit Theory by F. A. Benson and D. Harrison. Edward Arnold (Publishers) Ltd.

Network Analysis and Synthesis by Louis Weinberg. McGraw-Hill Publishing Co. Ltd.

The Theory of Networks in Electrical Communication and Other Fields by F. E. Rogers. Macdonald & Co. (Publishers) Ltd.
Electrical Engineers Handbook by H. Pender and K. L. McIlwain. Chapman & Hall Ltd.

Analogue computers

Principles of Analogue Computation by G. W. Smith and R. C. Wood. McGraw-Hill Publishing Co. Ltd.
Electronic Computers—Principles and Applications by T. E. Ivall. Iliffe Books Ltd.

Mathematics

An Introduction to the Laplace Transformation, with Engineering Applications by J. C. Jaeger. Methuen & Co. Ltd.
Mathematics for Higher National Certificate, Vol. II (*Electrical*) by S. W. Bell and H. Matley. Cambridge University Press.
Advanced National Certificate Mathematics, Vol. II by J. Pedoe. English Universities Press Ltd.